New book releases are free the first 48 hours. Every month, there is a free download on Kindle. To know of new releases and dates for free downloads, please subscribe at

www.TessaCason.com

Tessa Cason
5694 Mission Ctr. Rd. #602-213
San Diego, CA. 92108
www.TessaCason.com
Tessa@TessaCason.com



LEGAL NOTICE AND DISCLAIMER:

From author and publisher: The information in this book is not intended to diagnose or treat any particular disease and/or condition. Nothing contained herein is meant to replace qualified medical or psychological advice and/or services. The author and publisher do not assume responsibility for how the reader chooses to apply the techniques herein. Use of the information is at the reader's discretion and discernment. The author and publisher specifically disclaim any and all liability arising directly or indirectly from the use or application contained in this book.

Nothing contained in this book is to be considered medical advice for any specific situation. This information is not intended as a substitute for the advice or medical care of a Physician prior to taking any personal action with respect to the information contained in this book. This book and all of its contents are intended for educational and informational purpose only. The information in this book is believed to be reliable, but is presented without guaranty or warranty.

By reading further, you agree to release the author and publisher from any damages or injury associated with your use of the material in this book.

# 200 EFT Tapping Statements™ for PTSD

Tessa Cason, MA

# My EFT Tapping Story

I established a life coaching practice in 1996 when life coaching was in its infancy. After several years, I realized that exploration, discovery, knowledge, and awareness did not equate to change and transformation for my clients.

At the time, I knew that our beliefs preceded our thoughts and feelings, actions and reactions, choices and decisions. I knew that our beliefs were "stored" in the subconscious. Being aware of our dysfunctional beliefs and *wanting* to change them did not change the dysfunctional beliefs. To truly heal and transform our lives, we need to change the dysfunctional beliefs, our programming, on a subconscious level.

I needed a tool or technique that could help with this. I visited a friend who managed a bookstore and told her of my dilemma, and that I needed something to help my clients truly change and transform their lives. She reached for a book on the counter, near the register. "People have been raving about this book on EFT, Emotional Freedom Technique. Try it and see if it can help your clients."

In the 1990s, the internet was not an everyday part of our lives. Popular books sold more by word of mouth than any other means. Managing a bookstore, my friend knew what worked and what did not work. I trusted my friend, so I purchased the book.

As I read the book and discovered that EFT was tapping your head, I was unsure if this was the technique that would help my clients. I had some adventurous and forgiving clients whom I taught how to tap. When **every single client** returned for their next appointment and shared how different their lives had been that week because of tapping, I took notice! I was intrigued.

I learned that the first statement we needed to tap was: "It's not okay or safe for my life to change."

I learned that when a tapping statement did not clear, it meant there were other dysfunctional beliefs preventing the statement from clearing. When a statement didn't clear, I would turn the statement into a question.

I learned that for EFT Tapping to work, we needed to find the cause of an issue.

I learned that clearing an emotional memory was different from clearing dysfunctional beliefs.

Clients started asking for tapping homework. I wrote out statements for them to tap. Soon, I had a library of tapping statements on different emotional issues.

I have been a Life Coach since 1996 and an EFT Practitioner since 2000. EFT has proven to be an effective, powerful tool to change our dysfunctional beliefs, desensitize painful emotions and memories, and truly change our lives.

# Table of Contents

# Chapter 1
# Intro

If you suffer from PTSD, seek professional, qualified assistance to deal with the pain that you are enduring.

The role of the physical body is to keep us alive. The body breathes for us, pumps our heart for us, regulates our body temperature, digests our food, and converts our food into energy. All without conscious thought.

The role of the physical body is to keep us safe. When our hand gets too close to a flame, the body automatically pulls the hand back to safety. When our face is submerged in water, our body stops breathing to prevent the body from inhaling water. All without conscious thought.

The role of the physical body is to keep us alive and safe. When it perceives anything as a threat, the body automatically goes into survival mode, fight-flight-freeze, to prepare us to either fight, run away, or play dead. The body begins to breathe faster. Our awareness is heightened. The pulse and heart rate quickens. Survival mode is automatic...without conscious thought.

All of the above is automatic, without conscious thought. We don't have to tell the body to breathe. It knows that we need air. We don't tell the body to heighten our awareness when threatened. It knows that we are in danger.

Dr. John Montgomery says, "Biologically and evolutionarily, all 'negative,' or distressing, emotions, like fear, disgust, or anxiety, can be thought of as 'survival-mode' emotions: they signal to the body and brain that our survival and well-being may be at risk."

Distressing emotions, such as fear, alert the physical body that our survival may be at risk. When we feel fearful, the physical body automatically, without conscious thought, goes into survival mode.

In survival mode, the rational mind disengages. Fear is valued. We use anger to keep people at a safe distance. We become hyper-vigilant. We are constantly on edge. Our guard is always up. Fear, anger, depression, anxiety, and avoidance become our constant companions. We are only able to focus on the immediate tasks at hand.

Long-range goals are not even on the horizon. The ability to interact with other people is risky. Relaxing could mean death. Enjoying life and thriving is not possible. Positive emotions, such as love, joy, serenity, happiness, and hope, do not exist.

In survival mode, the survival emotions of fear, anger, and anxiety flood the body. We view the world through the veil of fear.

When we are experiencing distressing emotions,
such as fear, anger, anxiety, shame, and/or self-pity,
this can throw us into survival mode.

Even though the first section described the behaviors and consequences associated with the survival mode of fight, flight, or freeze, these are also the symptoms of post-traumatic stress disorder (PTSD).

PTSD is when we are stuck, continuously, in survival mode.
The body is not able to shut off the automatic responses.

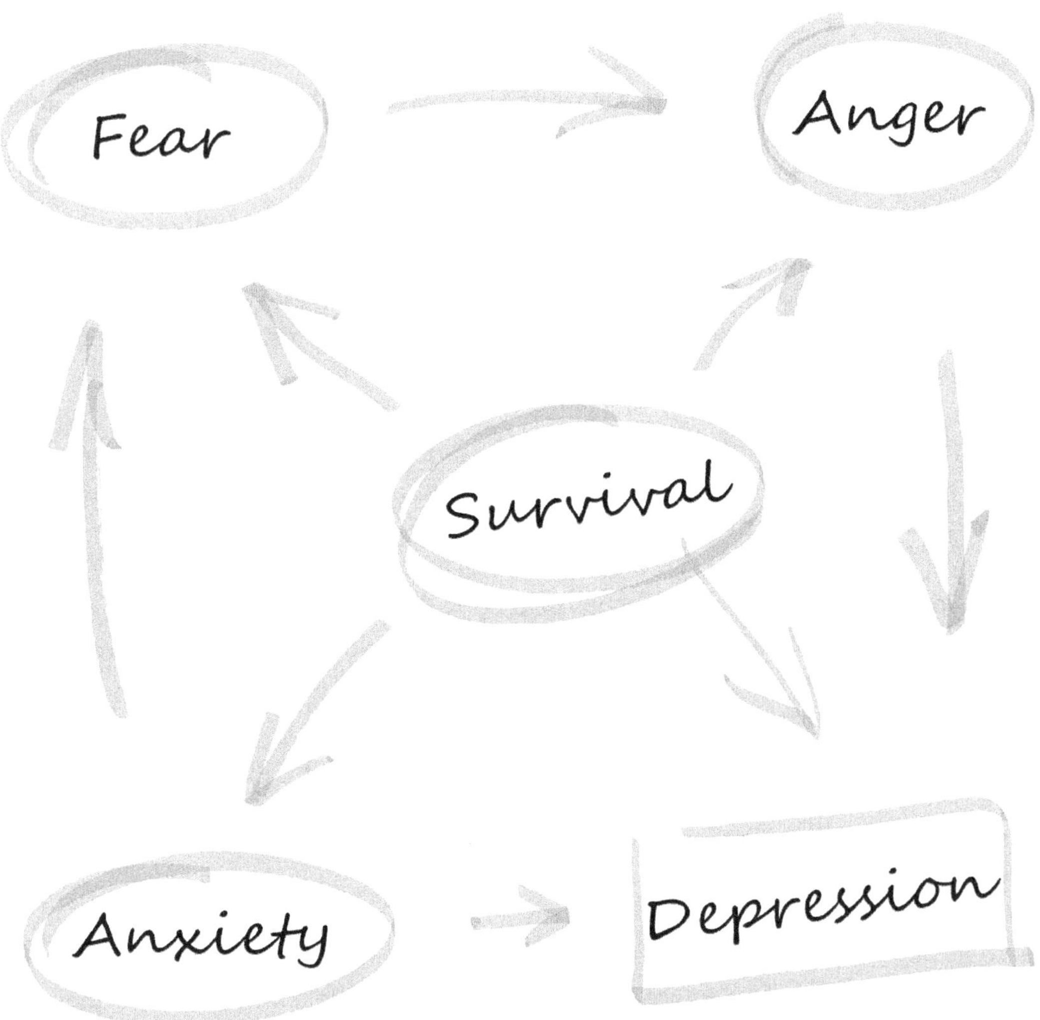

As much as we may not want to age, the body will automatically age. Our desire to stay young and youthful has no bearing on whether we age or not.

The same is true with PTSD. Simply NOT wanting to be stuck in survival with PSTD does not shut off the automatic responses.

The potential exists for anyone who is in any LIFE-THREATENING SITUATION, in which they fear for their life and BELIEVE their death is imminent, to experience PTSD. This could include:

* Being told we have cancer
* A car accident
* Military service
* A violent parent
* Victim of rape
* Being bullied
* Natural disaster
* Being bitten by a vicious dog
* A school shooting
* A terrorist attack
* Death of a spouse
* Death of a parent

The potential exists for anyone witnessing an event, in which others die senselessly and we feel our personal safety in the world is challenged, to also develop PTSD. This includes first responders.

There are a number of wonderful books that cover every possible facet of PTSD. My efforts here are not to duplicate or regurgitate what has already been expertly explored, examined, researched, discussed, and written by others far more competent than myself.

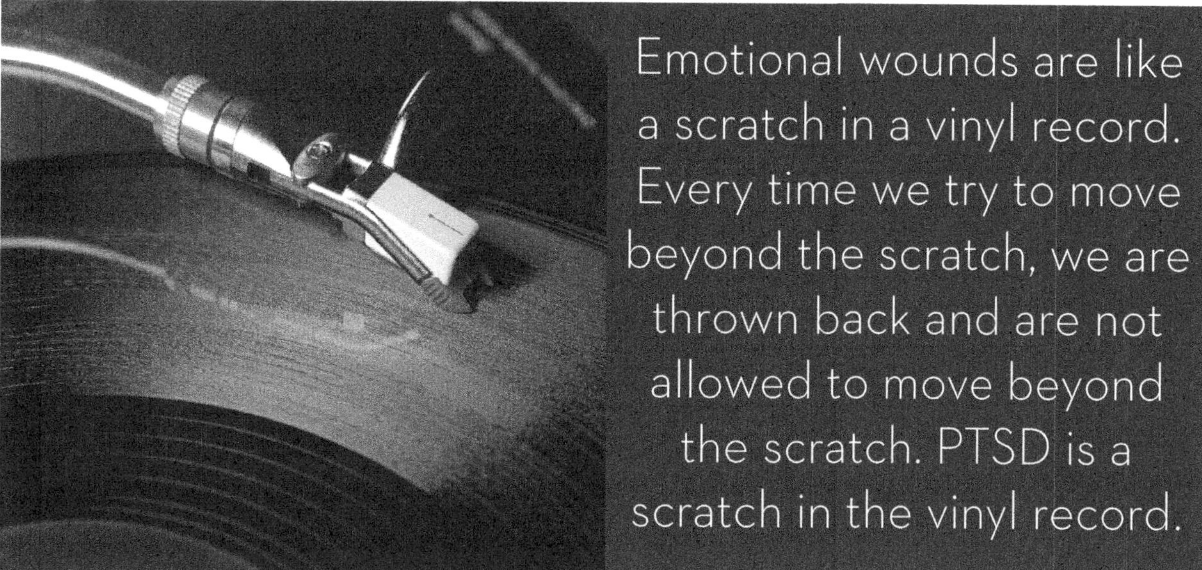

Emotional wounds are like a scratch in a vinyl record. Every time we try to move beyond the scratch, we are thrown back and are not allowed to move beyond the scratch. PTSD is a scratch in the vinyl record.

# Power of 3: Issue – Cause – Effect

In regard to being stuck emotionally, unable to move beyond the scratch on the vinyl record, there is a "cause" and "result." With every issue in our lives, there is a cause and the result of the cause. I call this the Power of 3.

With PTSD, our survival is at stake. As a result of our survival being threatened, we feel disempowered to thrive. We can only survive. The result of our survival being threatened is feeling disempowered.

Sometimes, the cause can also be the result. If we switch the previous statement around, making disempowerment the cause, the result could be feeling stuck in survival. When stuck in survival, it is nearly impossible to thrive and flourish.

When we are caught in survival, fear is a prevalent emotion. When we feel disempowered, anger is just beneath the surface.

To heal, thrive, and flourish, we need to address not only the PTSD but also survival, feeling disempowered, anger, and fear.

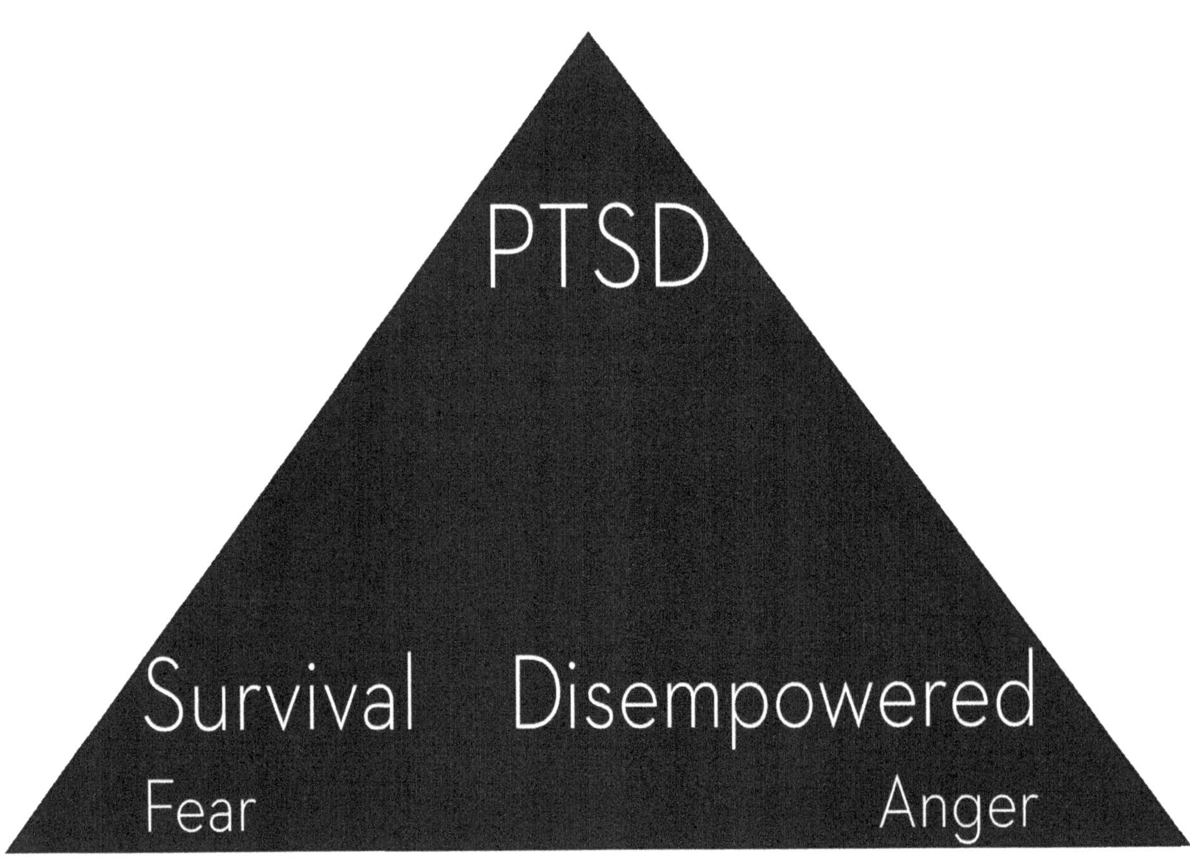

## Why Might Someone Be More Prone To PTSD?

All of us will have traumatic situations throughout our lives. Being scolded by a parent, bullied and humiliated by a peer, or having our hearts broken when a romantic relationship ends are all opportunities to learn coping tools and skills to manage stress. Those who may not have developed the skills to cope and manage stress when younger might be more prone to PTSD.

LIFE-THREATENING TRAUMATIC EVENT

Mission: Keep the body alive and safe.
Coping and Managing Stress Skills: Weak
Solution: Activate Survival Mode

Cause: Weak coping and managing stress skills.
Result: Activation of the Survival Mode.

## Can PTSD Be Healed Forever?

From my experience working with clients, including myself, who have been traumatized and stuck in PTSD, I can say with absolute certainty—Yes.

PTSD can be healed. There is no magic pill or drug. Someone cannot wave a magic wand and heal our PTSD. Someone else cannot do the work for us. It does require an effort from the one who is stuck in PTSD to do the work.

Where do we begin to heal PTSD? By deactivating the survival mode. So, how do we deactivate the survival mode that is continuously running? First, we have to desensitize and decrease the emotional response. Secondly, we need to learn new tools and skills to cope with and manage stress.

Healing PTSD is a process in which we must desensitize, decrease, and heal the survival response.

How do we desensitize and decrease the emotional response? The best method that I have found to do so is EFT tapping. I have witnessed the success of EFT tapping in healing rape victims, soldiers, accident victims, and others caught in PTSD.

Dr. Dawson Church, Ph.D. has conducted research that has demonstrated the value of EFT for addressing PTSD. On his website, he reviews many research projects for EFT and PTSD: http://www.eftuniverse.com/research-and-studies/eft-research

HEALING IS NOT ABOUT MANAGING SYMPTOMS.
IT'S ABOUT **ALLEVIATING** THE **CAUSE** OF THE SYMPTOMS

# Personal Power

Being empowered is not about physical, brute strength. It is not about the number and height of our successes and accomplishments. It is not about fame, the house we live in, the car we drive, or the clothes we wear.

BEING EMPOWERED IS THE STRENGTH, SUBSTANCE, AND CHARACTER OF OUR INNER BEING.

IT IS KNOWING THAT WHATEVER LIFE THROWS AT US, WE WILL PREVAIL.

All of us will have events that will challenge our ability to survive—physically, mentally, and emotionally. The manner in which we handle, survive, and grow from these challenges reveals how comfortable we are with being empowered. Below is one woman's story of discovering and learning how to be empowered.

As a working, single mom, Tiffany did the best she could raising her daughter, Summer, who was now nearing the tween years. Six months previously, she had moved the two of them into the home of her boyfriend. Everything was going well...until the night she came home early to find her boyfriend molesting her daughter. At that instant, she grabbed her daughter, ran out the door, called the police, and took her daughter to the nearest hospital.

In an instant, Tiffany's and Summer's lives were changed forever. Working paycheck to paycheck, the financial resources were not immediately available to find a new home. She had to ask friends and family for assistance and support, a humbling experience for Tiffany. The situation stripped Tiffany of her self-confidence. Her ability to trust others was shaken, and daily, she suffered the shame of creating an unsafe environment for her daughter.

Yet, Tiffany realized that she had a choice. She could be the victim and feel sorry for herself, or she could take responsibility. Tiffany took a deep breath and surrendered to the current situation that she found herself in.

Surrendering taught her about acceptance; needing assistance from others taught her to be open to receive. She was grateful and surprised by the kindness of others and their willingness to help when she needed their help the most.

"This event shook me to my core," Tiffany said. "It was a huge wake-up call, a realization that I needed to live my life in Truth. I realized that the events themselves were neutral. What was important was my response to the events. I knew I didn't want more of what I had.

"My desire was for change, so I could manifest a different life. It took mindful awareness, sometimes moment-to-moment, of how each choice felt to me. I had to weigh each against the idea: 'If I put this out into the Universe, is this what I want back?' This daily, sometimes hourly, practice of constantly assessing and experimenting brought me great confidence and faith in my ability to handle anything. This gave me a tremendous amount of personal power."

After reflecting on her story, she added, "Knowing that I had the power of choice created a sense of peace for me. Though cash was in short supply, I felt blessed, thankful, and prosperous as a result of the generosity and graciousness of others. I am not sure if this means my character was being revealed or if the experience built my character."

# Fear

Fear is a self-protection mechanism. It is an internal alarm system that alerts us to potential harm. When used *correctly*, the word "fear" refers specifically to the feeling of arousal that we experience in response to a clear and present danger in our external environment. During the experience of fear, the danger is *specific* and outside of ourselves. The sense of self is intact and the mind is fully operational.

Fear triggers the primitive fight-flight mechanism, releasing a surge of adrenaline to prepare the body to deal with a physical threat. Respiration becomes deeper, the pulse rate increases, and the blood pressure rises instantly. Blood supply is directed away from the stomach and intestines to the heart and is pumped to the muscles and lungs. Adrenaline is excreted from the adrenals, and sugar is freed from the reserves in the liver. All this to combat a threat to our well-being.

All fears begin as anxiety. Fear is something tangible, whereas anxiety is intangible, something that is difficult to put our finger on. Fear is *anxiety* that has found a specific threat to respond to. Fear describes the emotion that we feel when we are actually in danger. All other fears, those other than when we are actually in danger, are considered anxiety. With anxiety, the threat is vague and nebulous.

Fear does not exist in the present. Fear puts us in the future. Something from the past has been remembered. This memory triggers the fear that the same thing will happen again. We are fearful that the ending this time won't be any different than it was before. We are fearful that we will have to go through the same situation again, and we won't be able to handle it any better than the last time. We are fearful that we will experience the same pain, hurt, and devastation all over again.

When we are not in present time, we are in the fear of the future or the anger of the past. Courage, determination, awareness, focus, resilience, wisdom, confidence, discernment, insight—all these traits are only available in present time.

# Anger

Anger and frustration are natural emotions. Anger is not in itself right or wrong, healthy or unhealthy, appropriate or inappropriate. It is the *expression* of anger that makes it right or wrong, healthy or unhealthy, appropriate or inappropriate. Unhealthy anger is when anger is directed toward another to be hurtful and do harm. Wrong and inappropriate anger is when anger is violent and used to punish, intimidate, control, and manipulate.

Anger that is repressed and aggressive is unhealthy anger. It is unhealthy to stuff, ignore, and/or pretend the anger does not exist.

* Resentment is unexpressed anger.

* Passive-aggressive anger is anger meant to inflict pain.

* Rage is abusive anger filled with feelings of fear, sadness, shame, inadequacy, guilt, and/or loss.

* Depression is anger that we think we would get in trouble for having, thus depressing the anger.

* Guilt is anger that we don't feel we have a right to have.

* Apathy is suppressed anger.

*Worry is anticipated anger.

* Anxiety is a combination of four things: unidentified anger, hurt, fear, and self-pity. We expect error, rejection, and humiliation...and actually start to anticipate it.

Unresolved anger can lead to serious physical and mental health problems, such as heart disease, stroke, depression, and anxiety.

Suppressed anger can lead to depression, violence, or obsession. Old, suppressed anger can emerge at any time in response to a present situation. The response may be inappropriate, reactive, and have nothing to do with the present situation.

# Chapter 2
# Jake's Remembrance of George and Helen

Hi. My name is Jake. I want to tell you a story of courage.

I am an administrator of a small medical clinic in upstate New York. As the administrator, it is my responsibility to greet new patients and give them a tour of the facility. One spring day, I had the privilege of meeting and escorting Helen and George through our facility. I remember the day vividly as if it were yesterday, yet it's been over ten years now. It was a beautiful spring day. The temperature was just right—not too hot, not too cold. The snow had melted, and the flowers were beginning to bloom.

George was checking into our facility. The doctors in New York, where he and Helen resided, had told George to go home and put his affairs in order. Instead, George came to us.

George had a rich baritone voice. At the age of 56, he still had a full head of hair, although it was completely white now. His infectious laughter could be heard down the corridors. Even though George was battling cancer, he had a friendly word for everyone.

George was a fascinating man with an even more fascinating history. He was one of the original pioneers of the digital age and actually had more than a dozen patents. Rarely did my contact with patients extend after the first day, yet I found myself wandering down to George's room on a daily basis.

George made history come alive. Talking to him about the digital age would be like talking to Henry Ford thirty years after he designed and built the Model T. How fortunate I felt to be able to spend time with this legend!

And Helen? Helen made me smile. She was a spry and youthful 56-year-old who didn't look a day over 39. Her manners conveyed her grace and elegance. Petite, slender, and physically fit, Helen was a joy to be around. She always had a compliment for everyone, particularly those who were involved in George's care.

As children, George and Helen were next-door neighbors and spent a lot of time playing together. Televisions weren't a household item yet. George was always curious about how things worked and took apart anything his parents had not put a "Do Not Touch" sign on. Helen was his assistant. She would hand George the tools he requested. "Screwdriver," George would shout, and Helen would hand him the screwdriver. Yes, she knew the name of each and every tool. George made sure she did.

Halfway through their junior year of high school, Helen said to George, "You have to ask me to the prom!"

A little surprised, George responded, "Why?"

"'Cause if you don't, Randy Tucker is going to ask me, and I don't want to go with Randy Tucker. If you ask me, I can tell Randy that I already have a date."

Wanting to be the hero, George said, "Ms. Helen Grant, will you do me the honor of being my date for the prom?"

To both of their surprise, they had a wonderful time at the prom, dancing and talking all night. In the wee hours of the morning when they returned home, Helen gave George permission to kiss her. As the saying goes, the rest was history.

When George and Helen graduated from high school in 1962, they decided that George should enlist in the military. Helen's mom was quite ill, and her dad needed help with her care. So, Helen stayed behind to care for her aging parents.

During the interview with the military recruiter, the recruiter realized that George had a very quick, problem-solving type of intellect and asked George to take an aptitude test. Having the test results verify what the recruiter already knew, he sent George to a unique school to learn about computers. In 1962, computers were not a part of our everyday lives, as they are now.

After George completed his service, he returned home to New York City, married Helen, and went to work for IBM. When George wasn't at work, he was tinkering in his own workshop at home. By the time George was 29, he had sold one of his inventions, which allowed him the opportunity to stay home and tinker in his workshop all day long.

George would be so involved in his creations that he had no concept of time. If Helen didn't bring lunch to George, he would never know that it was time to eat. Helen's role was to take care of George. George took care of everything else.

One day when I went to visit George, Helen was out for her run. I asked George, "The doctors in New York suggested getting your affairs in order. Have you, George?"

George looked at me as if I had struck him and said, "No, Jake. If I prepare for death, that's inviting death into my life. I am not ready to die, nor do I want to give death any indication that I am ready to follow him into the afterlife. I have no intention of dying!"

This struck me as odd. George, though very creative, also had an analytical side that created a dozen detailed patents. His inventions were forward thinking, yet his physical thoughts seemed retro. Seriously? He thought if he organized his earthly affairs that he would be inviting death into his life?

From George's intake form, I knew that neither Helen nor George had any living relatives. Both had younger brothers who were killed in Vietnam. George and Helen never had children and both sets of parents were deceased.

I am getting off track here. This story is about courage. Not George's, but Helen's.

After spending a splendid week with George and Helen, their time with us came to an end. There wasn't anything more we could do. The doctors in New York had been very thorough in their treatment of George's cancer.

A month after George and Helen left, I received a note from Helen that George had passed away, including the date of the memorial service. I sent Helen a note with my condolences and let her know that I would see her at George's memorial service.

When I arrived at the church, I was surprised to see so many people at the service, as well as camera crews outside. As I approached Helen, I could see the terror in her eyes. "Jake," she whispered, "I don't know 95% of these people. My friends and our friends, George and mine, are here. Who are the rest of these people? Why are there camera crews outside?"

I wasn't quite sure how to respond. "Your husband is a legend" didn't seem the right thing to say. "Your husband helped usher in the digital age" didn't seem appropriate either. Did she not know the importance George had in all of our lives? I was able to say, "Maybe to pay tribute to George."

At that moment, Ellen joined Helen and me at the front of the church. Helen introduced Ellen as her best friend of twenty years. After greeting each other, Ellen gently guided Helen to the front pew so the service could begin. I took a seat behind Helen in the second row.

Photos of George and an abundance of flowers decorated the front of the church. Once Helen was seated, the minister began the service. At the conclusion of the service, the minister said, "Friends of George and Helen have arranged a reception in the reception hall, and everyone is invited to attend."

Out of respect, everyone stood and waited for Helen to stand and make her way to the hall. More flowers were scattered throughout the hall. The attendance book was placed on a table at the entrance. As people entered the hall and signed the book, they left cards and thick envelopes on the table.

Friends of George and Helen had set up a buffet of food in the hall. A spontaneous receiving line was created as people approached Helen to tell her how her husband had changed their lives. Some told her how George had delivered computers to a whole classroom of children, and their lives were forever changed. Others told her that George gave them money, so they could pay their rent without any obligation of repayment. And others told her the wise words George had spoken to them at a time when they thought they could not go on living.

They were alive because of George's compassion and concern. There were people from all walks of life, all colors, and all economic levels in attendance.

As story after story was described to Helen, tears caressed her cheeks. She was in awe of a man she never knew existed. He never shared any of those stories with her. Helen was gracious, receiving the stories from everyone who wanted to share with her.

While Helen was occupied with listening to stories about George, I was able to have a conversation with Ellen. She told me that since George's passing, Ellen or another friend had been with Helen. Helen was not handling George's death well at all. Even though she knew that the doctors had told George to get his affairs in order, George had not done so. George didn't think that he would die, and Helen was not prepared for his death. She swung from shock to disbelief, tears to anger, depression to realization that he was gone, anxiety back to anger or depression. Helen was on an emotional roller coaster that traveled through the full spectrum of emotions.

I shared the conversation I had with George when he was at the clinic a month ago. I added, "He thought he was preparing for death if he put his affairs in order." I asked Ellen, "Did he leave a will?"

"Not that any of us can find. My husband, Herbert, and I plan on tackling their affairs this week to see if we can sort everything out. George was meticulous with his inventions and patents but not so much with their personal affairs," Ellen said with a sigh.

Since I had taken the week off to enjoy New York City, I offered to help.

Ellen was very appreciative of my offer. She wrote down Helen's address, and we planned on meeting later that day at Helen's to begin. Ellen saw that the line was just about to disband and rejoined Helen. Helen looked very tired, and her face was streaked with lines of mascara. Herbert commented that maybe now would be a good time to depart. Helen stood up, straight and tall, took Herbert's arm, and said, "I am tired, Herbert. I am ready."

I returned to my hotel off Central Park, changed into some comfortable clothes, and strolled through the park. My thoughts kept drifting back to Helen, to the terror in her eyes before the service and the compassion and grace that she exhibited at the reception. Then I thought of the conversation that I had with George about refusing to prepare for death because it would invite death into his life and the conversation that I had with Ellen, in which I found out that George had not left a will.

Later that day, I found the two-story brick home on a quiet street lined with mature trees. Ellen answered the door and invited me into an exquisite space. Talk about an open concept.

The whole bottom floor was unlike anything I had ever seen before. Helen's elegance and grace were evident in every square inch. Everything was beautifully decorated and coordinated, from the color on the walls to the style of the furniture, the accessories to the décor. It was a massive space that encompassed the kitchen, living room, formal dining room, and casual living room space. Nothing seemed to be out of place. Everything was very neat and clean.

I felt my eyes go wide and heard Ellen say, "Beautiful, isn't it?"

"That's an understatement," I said in heavenly awe.

"Helen has been asleep since we returned from the service. Let me show you what we are up against. Follow me to George's workshop." With that, Ellen walked across the room toward the backyard. Sliding the glass door open, I followed her into another exquisite space. The yard was awash with color from the blossoming flowers and green plants. Upon seeing my delight, Ellen said, "All Helen. She has a green thumb and a gardener who comes once a week."

Across the yard was another building with a brick façade. As Ellen opened the door, she spoke to Herbert, "Herbert, this is Jake." Herbert stood, and we shook hands. Ellen continued, "Jake was the administrator at the medical clinic upstate that George visited last month."

Herbert spoke, "George mentioned your clinic and you. He felt at peace at your clinic. You must have been the young man interested in history. George can weave a story or two!" Herbert said, a mix of chuckling and smiling.

After shaking hands with Herbert, I started to look around and couldn't believe the disorder that I saw around me. Both Ellen and Herbert noticed my bewilderment. "Quite a bit of difference between the house and the workshop," commented Ellen. She continued, "Helen's responsibilities were to take care of George and the house. She did both very well. On the other hand," Ellen paused as she surveyed the room, "Helen wasn't allowed to touch anything in this room. George knew where everything was."

With a heavy sigh, Herbert added, "But now, George isn't here. We can't find any rhyme or reason to George's system, if he had any to begin with."

"Herbert, give Jake a tour while I go wake Helen. She won't be able to sleep tonight if I don't wake her now." At the door, Ellen turned around and added, "Why don't the two of you come over to the house in about 30 minutes." With that, she waved goodbye and was off.

I didn't know what to think or what I had volunteered for! The chaos looked like it would take six months to sort through. With a laugh, Herbert said, "A little overwhelming, isn't it?"

I shook my head in disbelief. To George, I suppose it didn't look like a mess. To the rest of us, it looked to be in a state of total and utter disarray. It took Herbert 30 minutes to give me a tour of the chaos, and he added, "What we are looking for is a will or legal documents, such as deeds, trusts to show ownership of the house, his patents, or maybe an attorney's name. I haven't really had a chance to dig in yet. Helen is too distraught to be of any help. She's still in shock over George's death. She hasn't been back to the workshop yet. I don't think she can handle it at this time."

We decided to close the door and join Ellen and Helen in the main house. Helen's eyes were bloodshot, and she was weary from the day. Her eyelids weren't much good at keeping the tears from spilling out or running down her cheeks. As graciously as Helen could, she thanked me for coming.

"Ellen said that you have offered to help sort out George's workshop. That's very generous of you," Helen said. "Are you not needed back at the clinic?"

"Being the administrator gives me designation authority. I have designated my responsibilities to other people while I am here," I said.

"Then, you must stay in one of our guest rooms upstairs. George would want you to," Helen said with a weak smile.

Seemingly years away, Helen distractedly said, "I have been George's wife for 34 years. I don't know who I am any longer if I am not George's wife." And with that, a few tears escaped, rolling down Helen's drawn face.

Looking up at Herbert, Helen asked, "Herbert, do I have to move? This is the only home that I have known. We moved into this house 27 years ago. Where would I go? Can I stay? Will I be evicted?" asked a confused Helen.

"Helen," Herbert said softly. "I don't know. I guess I just assumed that you and George purchased your home. Do you know if you did? Do you know if there is a mortgage?" asked Herbert.

"I don't know. George handled everything. I don't know," Helen said as she looked down at her hands lying in her lap. Remembering that she was in the middle of a conversation, she looked up at Herbert and said, "I have a credit card to purchase everything that we need, and George handled the finances. I take care of the house and of George, of course. George needed me to take care of him. I would take lunch to him and remind him to come in for dinner. I took care of George. George took care of everything else, including the finances." Helen's mind could not comprehend anything further at this time.

To distract Helen from her thoughts, Ellen spoke up and said that she thought it was a great idea if I moved into one of the upstairs bedrooms. "Jake, would that work for you?" she asked me.

I wasn't sure how to respond, or what I thought, so I said, "Okay." With that, Ellen said that Herbert would drive me to my hotel now so I could check out and be back before dinner. So soon? I thought. Yet, I responded in the affirmative.

While in the car on the way to my hotel, Herbert filled me in on Helen's state of mind. "At one moment, she's like a top that is spinning from one thought to another. Then, waves of panic set in. She can shift into anger at George for not preparing her for his death. George left no will and no instructions, not even all the important documents in one place so we could find them. We don't know if there is a safety deposit box someplace."

I asked, "You mentioned in the workshop to look for the name of an attorney. Do you know if George had an attorney?"

"He never mentioned anyone involved with his professional life. He kept the two separate, his personal and professional lives," Herbert added.

"At the clinic, Helen seemed so strong and self-assured. Grief takes a heavy toll on everyone—and to add this chaos that George left behind..." I paused. I wasn't sure of what to say.

Herbert spoke up, "Even the mail is a traumatic occurrence. Since George's death, a couple of bank statements have come in, a statement for a mutual fund has arrived, and a couple of bills. We don't know if George had life insurance. We don't know if they own their home. If they did, was there a mortgage? Some of the monthly expenditures look to be set up on autopay. But how many items and how long before the bank accounts are depleted is an unknown," Herbert said, taking a deep breath in and exhaling.

"Does Helen know any of these answers?" I asked, hoping there was a glimmer of hope around the dark cloud.

"Nothing, literally nothing," said an exhausted Herbert. "Ellen and I were some of George and Helen's closest friends. Helen is in no way capable emotionally to handle any of this chaos. This last week, since George's death, Ellen has tried to be a stabilizing force for Helen's roller coaster emotions." Stopped at a red light, Herbert took off his glasses and rubbed his eyes.

With a sigh, he added, "I have been in the workshop by myself, trying to make sense of George's lack of organization. I truly am thankful that you volunteered to help." With a chuckle, he asked, "You did volunteer, didn't you? Or did Ellen volunteer you? You may have noticed that she has a way of getting what she wants!"

Thinking back, I said, "I don't know. I can't remember whether I volunteered or Ellen volunteered me. Either way, Herbert, I am here to help. Being an administrator at the clinic, I know my way around financial statements!"

We rode in silence for a few blocks. Realizing that I knew nothing about Herbert, I asked him what he did professionally and how they had met Helen and George, if it wasn't through business. He said they moved in next door to George and Helen twenty years ago and had been close friends ever since. Professionally, he was a psychologist. Like me, he had control of his schedule and had cancelled everything until he and Ellen could help get Helen normalized.

We rode in silence for a few more blocks, and then I asked, "Herbert, you might not be someone who can help Helen emotionally through her grief, anger, depression, and fears, but is there someone else in your office who might?"

"Jake, you have asked the same question that Ellen and I have been pondering this last week. Have you ever heard of EFT tapping? Emotional Freedom Technique?" asked Herbert.

"Yes. We have been using tapping in our clinic for several years now," I answered. I hoped he was going to tell me that he had someone in their office who knew EFT tapping. Over and over again, I had seen miraculous healings when someone tapped. I thought it just might be what the doctor ordered for Helen!

Herbert asked, "What has been your experience with tapping? Do you think it really works?"

I told Herbert that when the practitioner is trained to deal with dysfunctional emotions and beliefs, I had seen healing both physically and emotionally.

"We have a new practitioner in the office, and one of the tools that she uses is EFT tapping. Her name is Susan. Ellen thinks Susan would be able to help Helen. I am the one who has been dragging my feet because I wasn't sold on this tapping thing. But, since your experience is favorable, I think I will ask Helen if she would like to talk to Susan."

To make a long story short, Susan did come and work with Helen. Susan felt Helen was suffering from PTSD as a result of George's death and George not leaving his financial affairs in order. Susan came to the house quite frequently to help Helen deal with her sense of survival being threatened, her grief, anger, depression, and anxiety. Watching the courage Helen had to heal was like watching a bud blossom.

EFT tapping helped Helen feel whole and complete. She found her own identity. She began to take an interest in the work that George did. The stronger she felt, the more she could help Herbert, Ellen, and me sort through George's workshop. We never found a will or the name of an attorney. Helen contacted Herbert's attorney and began all the legal documentation that was needed. With the money that George made on the sale of his first patent, he had purchased the house. Helen's name was on the title, and they owned the home without a mortgage. The four of us were able to eventually put all the puzzle pieces together.

As much as I was in awe of George, I am more so in awe of Helen. To deal with the death of a spouse is traumatic in itself. To compound Helen's life, she also had to sort through her financial affairs at a time when she should have been allowed to grieve.

Helen wrote a book to empower other people to organize their lives in preparation for their death someday. The book is entitled The Greatest Gift You Can Give a Loved One - Prepare for Your Death. In the book, she shared her story of having to heal her grief and PTSD while being stuck in survival mode, wondering if each knock on the door was someone coming to evict her from her home.

It's been 10 years since George's death. Helen wanted to pay tribute to George and invited a few friends to do so. Helen and I stayed in touch after we finished sorting through George's workshop and putting her financial affairs in order. At the tribute, I gave this toast: "To Helen, a courageous woman of elegance, grace, compassion, and wisdom, who is now helping others to avoid the pain and suffering that she went through."

EFT
TAPPING

# Chapter 3
# EFT Tapping - Emotional Freedom Technique

EFT Tapping is a very easy technique to learn. It involves making a statement as we contact the body by either circling or tapping.

An EFT Tapping Statement has three parts:

Part 1: starts with "**Even though**" followed by

Part 2: a statement which could be the **dysfunctional emotion or belief**, and

Part 3: ends with "**I totally and completely accept myself**."

A complete statement would be, "**Even though I fear change, I totally and completely accept myself**."

## Instruction for the Short Form of EFT Tapping

The instructions below are for using the right hand. Reverse the directions to tap using the left hand. It is more effective, when we tap, to tap only one side rather than both.

### I. Set up - begin with circling or tapping the Side of the Hand:

A. With the fingertips of the right hand, find a tender spot below the left collar bone. Once the tender spot is identified, press firmly on the spot, moving the fingertips in a circular motion toward the left shoulder, toward the outside, clockwise. Tapping the side of the hand can also be used instead of the circling.

B. As the fingers circle and press against the tender spot or tap the side of the hand, repeat the tapping statement three times: "Even though, ___[tapping statement]___, I totally and completely accept myself." An example would be: "Even though I fear change, I totally and completely accept myself."

Side of the hand

Tender spot below the left collar bone

## II. Tapping:

A. After the third time, tap the following eight points, repeating the [tapping statement] at each point. Tap each point five – ten times:

1. The inner edge of the eyebrow, just above the eye. [I fear change.]
2. Temple, just to the side of the eye. [I fear change.]
3. Just below the eye (on the cheekbone). [I fear change.]
4. Under the nose. [I fear change.]
5. Under the lips. [I fear change.]
6. Under the knob of the collar bone. [I fear change.]
7. Three inches under the arm pit. [I fear change.]
8. Top back of the head. [I fear change.]

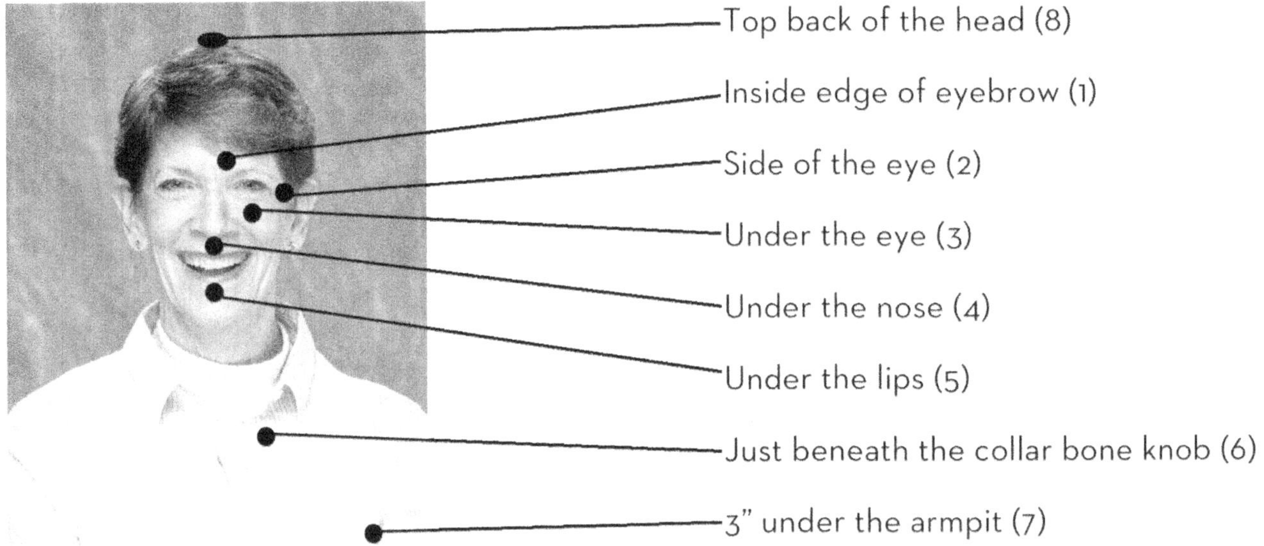


B. After tapping, take a deep breath. If you are not able to take a deep, full, satisfying breath, do eye rolls.

## III. Eye rolls

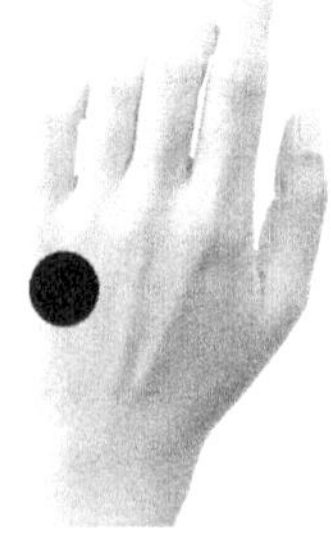

A. With one hand tap continuously on the **back** of the other hand between the fourth and fifth fingers.
B. Hold your head straight forward, eyes looking straight down.
C. For six seconds, roll your eyes from the floor straight up toward the ceiling while repeating the tapping statement. Keep the head straight forward, only moving the eyes.

## IV. Take another deep breath.

# Chapter 4
# EFT Tapping, Beliefs, and the Subconscious Mind

## EFT - Emotional Freedom Technique

EFT is a technique that allows us to change dysfunctional beliefs and emotions on a subconscious level. It involves making a statement while tapping different points along meridian paths.

The general principle behind EFT is that the cause of all negative emotions is a disruption in the body's energy system. By tapping on locations where several different meridians flow, we can release unproductive memories, emotions, and beliefs that cause the blockages.

## A Belief is...

**A belief** is a mental acceptance of, and conviction in, the Truth, actuality, or validity of something. It is what we believe to be true, whether it is Truth or not. A belief is a thought that influences energy all the time.

## A Dysfunctional Belief is...

**A dysfunctional belief** is a belief that takes us away from peace, love, joy, stability, acceptance, and harmony. It causes us to feel stressed, fearful, anxious, and/or insecure.

## The Conscious Mind is...

The conscious mind is the part of us that thinks, passes judgments, makes decisions, remembers, analyzes, has desires, and communicates with others. It is responsible for logic and reasoning, understanding and comprehension. The mind determines our actions, feelings, thoughts, judgments, and decisions **based on beliefs.**

## The Subconscious Mind is...

The subconscious is the part of the mind responsible for all our involuntary actions like our heartbeat and breathing rate. It does not evaluate, make decisions, or pass judgment. It just is. It does not determine if something is "right" or "wrong."

The subconscious is much like the software of a computer. On the computer keyboard, if we press the key for the letter "a," we will see the letter "a" on the screen, even though we may have wanted to see "t." Just as a computer can only do what it has been programmed to do, we can only do as we are programmed to do.

Our programming is determined by our beliefs. Beliefs and memories are "stored" in the subconscious.

## Three Rules of the Subconscious Mind

Three rules of the subconscious mind include:

1. Personal. It only understands "I," "me," "myself." First-person.
2. Positive. The subconscious does not hear the word "no." When you say, "I am not going to eat that piece of cake," the subconscious mind hears, "Yummm! Cake! I am going to eat a piece of that cake!"
3. Present time. Time does not exist for the subconscious. The only time it knows is "now," present time. "I'm going to start my diet tomorrow." "Tomorrow" never comes; thus, the diet never starts.

Beliefs precede all of our thoughts, feelings,
decisions, choices, actions, reactions,
and experiences...

Our beliefs and memories are stored
in the subconscious mind.

If we want to make changes in our lives,
we have to change the programming,
the dysfunctional beliefs in the subconscious.

Three rules of the Subconscious Mind:
Personal
Positive
Present time

# Chapter 5
# How Does EFT Tapping Work?

1. Acceptance: The last part of the tapping statement, we say, "I totally and completely accept myself." **Acceptance brings us into present time.** We can only heal if we are in present time.

2. Addresses the current dysfunctional beliefs on a subconscious level: To make changes in our lives, we have to change the dysfunctional beliefs on a subconscious level. The middle part of the tapping statements are the "instructions" for the subconscious. **To make changes in our lives, we only care what the subconscious hears.**

3. Pattern interrupt: Dysfunctional memories and/or beliefs block energy from flowing freely along the meridians. Tapping is a pattern interrupt that disrupts the flow of energy to allow our **body's own Infinite Wisdom to come forth for healing.** (Tapping both sides does not act as a pattern interrupt.)

4. Mis-direct: One role of the physical body is to protect us. When our hand is too close to a flame, our body automatically pulls our hand back to safety. An EFT Tapping statement that agrees with the current belief is more effective. The physical body is less likely to sabotage the tapping if it agrees with the current belief.

For the EFT Taping statement "I fear change":

* This statement appeases the physical body since it agrees with the current belief.
* The tapping disrupts the energy flow so our Truth can come forth.

The body will always gravitate to health, wealth, and well-being when the conditions allow it. EFT Tapping weeds the garden so the blossoms can bloom more easily and effortlessly.

# Chapter 6
# Benefits of Using EFT Tapping

* The last part of the statement is, "I totally and completely **accept** myself." **Acceptance** brings us into present time. Healing can only take place when we are in present time.

* By tapping, we are **calling forth our Truths.** The keyword here is "**our.**" Not anyone else's. If my name is "Lucas," tapping the statement "Even though my name is Troy," my name will not change to Troy.

* Tapping **calls forth our body's Infinite Wisdom**. When we cut our finger, our body knows how to heal the cut itself. Once the dysfunctional emotions, experiences, and beliefs have been "deleted," our body **automatically** gravitates to health, wealth, wisdom, peace, love, joy...

* By changing dysfunctional beliefs and emotions on a subconscious level, the changes we make with EFT are **permanent.**

* EFT Tapping can change:

  Beliefs
  Emotions
  Self-images
  Our story
  Thoughts
  Mind chatter
  Painful memories

* EFT Tapping can neutralize stored memories that block energy along the meridians.

* EFT Tapping can desensitize emotions. We might have a difficult person in our life who ignores us and/or criticizes us, so we tap the statement: "This difficult person [or their name] ignores and criticizes me."

  Tapping does not mean they will no longer ignore and/or criticize us; however, it can **desensitize us,** so we are no longer affected by their behavior. Once we have desensitized the emotions, our perception and mental thinking improve. We are better able to make informed decisions. We don't take and make everything personal. Our health is not negatively impacted. Our heart doesn't beat 100 beats/minute. Smoke stops coming out of our ears, and our faces don't turn red with anger and frustration.

# Chapter 7
# What We Say As We Tap Is VERY Important!

All of our beliefs are programmed into our subconscious minds. If we want to change our lives, we have to delete the dysfunctional beliefs on a subconscious level. The statements we make as we tap are the instructions for the subconscious mind.

THE TAPPING STATEMENTS WE WAY AS WE ARE TAPPING ARE CRITICAL FOR THIS TO HAPPEN!

Example: You get in a taxi. Several hours later, you still have not arrived at your destination. "*Why?*" you ask. Because you did not give the destination to the taxi driver!

Tapping without saying an adequate tapping statement is like riding in a cab without giving the cab driver our destination!

For EFT Tapping to be MOST EFFECTIVE the Tapping Statement is CRITICAL!

EFT Tapping allows us to delete the dysfunctional beliefs on a subconscious level. The statements we make as we tap are instructions to the subconscious mind so our Truth can come forth.

# Chapter 8
# Using a Negative EFT Tapping Statement

Our beliefs **precede** all of our thoughts, feelings, decisions, choices, actions, reactions, and experiences.

If we want to make changes in our lives, we have to change the dysfunctional beliefs. Our beliefs are stored in the subconscious.

To change our lives, to change a belief, we only care what the subconscious hears when we tap. The subconscious does not hear the word "no." When we say, "I am not going to eat that piece of cake," the subconscious hears, "Yummm, cake!"

Example, if we don't believe we have what it takes to be successful and we tap the statement, "I have what it takes to be successful," the body could sabotage the tapping. We could tap and it won't clear.

Instead, if the statement we make is, "I do not have what it takes to be successful," the "**not**" appeases the physical body and the subconscious hears, "I have what it takes to be successful!"

A tapping statement with the word "no" or "not" works best!

# Chapter 9
# EFT Tapping Statements Are Most Effective When They Agree With Current Beliefs

The EFT Tapping statement is **more successful when** it **is something the body currently believes.**

The body is less likely to sabotage an EFT Tapping statement that agrees with the current belief.

One role of the physical body is to protect us from harm. (For example, if our hand gets too close to a flame, our body will pull our hand back to safety.) The body is less likely to sabotage the statement and the process if the EFT Tapping statement agrees with the current belief. Thus, it appeases the physical body.

For example, if our desire is prosperity and wealth and we tap the statement, "I am prosperous now," the body could sabotage the tapping by forgetting what we were saying, getting easily distracted, or our mind chatter may remind us we are not prosperous. We could tap and the statement, most likely, will not clear.

If the statement we say is "I am not prosperous now," the "**not**" appeases the physical body, and the subconscious hears, "I am prosperous now!"

# Chapter 10
# The Very First EFT Tapping Statement to Tap

The very first EFT Tapping statement I have clients and students tap is, "It is not okay or safe for my life to change." I have muscle tested this statement with more than a thousand people. Not one person tested strong that it was okay or safe for their life to change. (Muscle testing is a way in which we can converse with the body, bypassing the conscious mind.)

How effective can EFT or any
therapy be if it is not okay or safe
for our lives to change?

Since our lives are constantly changing, if it is not okay or safe for our lives to change, every time our lives change, it creates stress for the body. Stress creates another whole set of issues for ourselves, our lives, and our bodies.

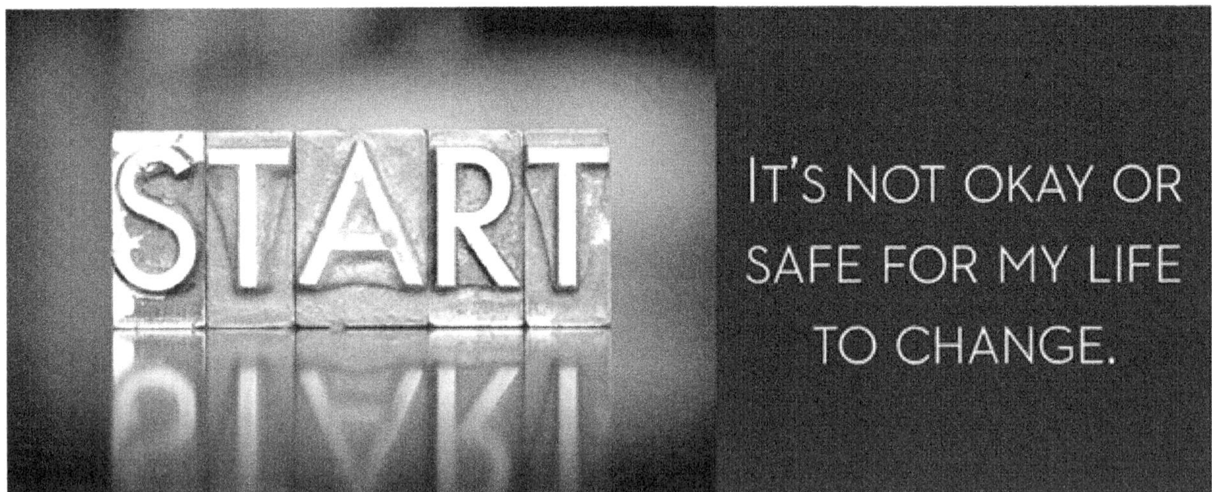

# Chapter 11
# One Statement per Round of EFT vs Multiple Statements per Round of EFT

## Laser-focused Tapping vs Round Robin Tapping

## Same Statement for all the Tapping Points in One Round vs Multiple Statements in One Round of Tapping (Scripts)

Two styles of tapping for different purposes. One style is best for healing dysfunctional beliefs. The other style is best for healing emotions, desensitizing a story, situation, and/or memory.

I found that the laser-focused, one statement for a round of tapping was most effective for healing the beliefs. Multiple statements per round of tapping is great at healing emotions, desensitizing a story, situation, and/or memory.

### Same Statement for All the Tapping Points in One Round

After tapping the statement, "It's not okay for my life to change," and we are able to take a deep breath, we know the statement cleared. Then we tap, "I'm not ready for my life to change," and we are not able to take a deep breath, most likely, the statement did not clear.

Knowing the statement did not clear, we can focus on the reasons, excuses, and/or beliefs about not being ready to change our lives.

* Maybe the changes we need to make would require more of us than we want to give.
* Maybe we don't feel we have the abilities we would need if our life changed.
* Maybe we don't feel our support system, the people in our life, would support the changes we want to make.

Follow-up tapping statements for "I'm not ready for my life to change" could be:

* I do not have the abilities change would require.
* I am afraid of change.
* Others will not support the changes I want to make in my life.
* I am not able to make the changes I want to make.
* I do not have the courage that change would require.
* I am too old to change.

Tapping the same statement at all eight points is most effective for clearing beliefs. When a statement does not clear, we can focus on the reasons, excuses, and/or dysfunctional beliefs that blocked the statement from clearing.

### Multiple Statements in One Round of Tapping (Scripts/Round Robin)

Tapping multiple statements in one round, also known as Scripts or Round Robin tapping, is excellent for healing a story, and desensitizing a memory or story.

Healing a broken heart, to desensitize the heartache of the break up, the following script/ statements could be said, one statement/point:

* My boyfriend broke up with me.
* I am heartbroken.
* He said he doesn't love me anymore.
* I do not know how I can go on without him.
* It hurts.
* I am sad he doesn't love me anymore.
* I am sad our relationship is over.
* I will never find anyone like him ever again.

### Reframing:

Reframing is a Neuro Linguistic Programming (NLP) term. It is a way to view and experience emotions, situations, and/or behaviors in a more positive manner.

At the end of round robin tapping, we can introduce statements to "reframe" the situation.

An example of reframing could be:

* I want this chocolate.
* Maybe eating chocolate is wanting to reconnect to my childhood.
* Maybe eating sugar is a way of being loved.
* Maybe I can find a different way of being loved.

Round robin tapping, scripts, can desensitize the hurt and pain. It can heal the pain of our story. It may not rewrite the beliefs. To clear out the beliefs, it would be necessary to look at the reasons the relationship didn't work and why our heart is broken, or why we crave chocolate.

Round robin/script tapping can also be done by just tapping the side of the hand.

## Side of Hand Tapping to Desensitize a Story, Situation, and/or Memory

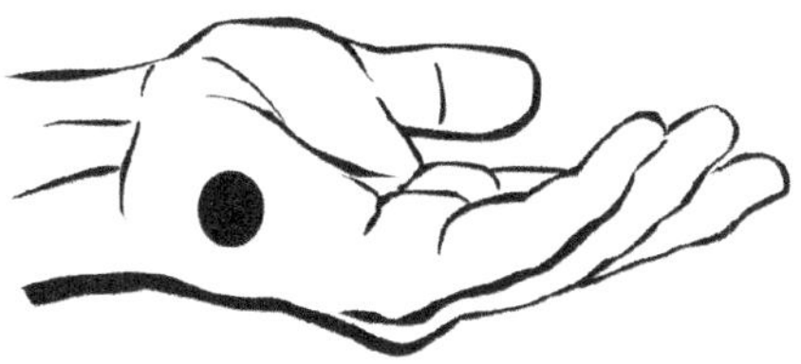

Just as in the round robin tapping/scripts, we said different statements, one after the other, we can say the same statements and just tap the side of the hand.

If a memory still "haunts" us, embarrasses us, and/or affects our actions in any way, this technique might be perfect to neutralize the memory.

For example:

As Sasha remembers the first dance she attended as a teen-ager, tears well up in her eyes. She starts to tap the side of the hand (SOH) as she tells her story:

My best friend, Samantha and I, were so excited about attending our first high school dance. We weren't old enough to drive so Sam's dad dropped us off in front of the high school auditorium where the dance was held.

*(Continue to tap the SOH)* We were in awe of how the auditorium was transformed into a palace. Sofas were placed around a hardwood dance floor in the center of the room. We promised each other we would be there for the other throughout the night so neither of us would be stranded alone.

*(Continue to tap the SOH)* Well, along came Billy McDaniels. Sam had had a crush on Billy since third grade. He asked her to dance and I never saw her again for the rest of the night.

*(Continue to tap the SOH)* Those three hours were probably the worst night of my entire life! No one asked me to dance. Every time I joined a group of girls, a new song would begin, and every one of them was asked to dance, everyone except me. I don't know why no one asked me to dance. I felt ugly, abandoned, and undesirable! Talk about being a wallflower. I thought I was invisible. I wanted to hide from embarrassment.

*(Continue to tap the SOH)* This was back in the days before cell phones. The auditorium didn't have a payphone to call my parents to come and get me. I had to endure three hours of humiliation watching every single girl be asked to dance EXCEPT me.

*(Continue to tap the SOH)* I never attended another high school dance again!

Whether we tap the side of the hand or the eight tapping points, the result is the same. Round robin tapping can desensitize emotions and memories very effectively.

There are different styles of EFT Tapping.
Find the style that works best for your desired result.

# Chapter 12
# Walking Backwards EFT (Backing Up)

As I was working with a client, they had an issue that was not clearing. Knowing that movement helps to clear issues, I decided to have the person stand up and walk backward. Literally, walk backward, step after step, facing forward while their feet moved backward.

Surprise, surprise, it worked. Every statement cleared as she backed up.

The next client came in. I had him walk backwards, and it worked with clearing issues for him as well. Both clients were somewhat athletic and did workout. I wanted to know if the Backing Up would work with non-athletic people. I was teaching an EFT class the next day. At the end of the class, we all backed up together. And, IT WORKED!

Let's say we want to process, "I will never be comfortable in the world." Stand up. Make sure nothing is behind you. Then walk backward while facing forward and say, "I will never be comfortable in the world. I will never be comfortable in the world. I will never be comfortable in the world. I will never be comfortable in the world." Repeat the phrase six - eight times.

When we back up, we say the same statement we would have made if we were tapping. We don't have to say the "Even though" or the last remainder phrase, "I totally and completely accept myself."

Walking forward represents forward movement in our lives. Walking backward represents the past.

Physical movement can help clear emotional issues and facilitate change.

Walking backward undoes the past and helps to clear, heal, and transform an issue in our lives.

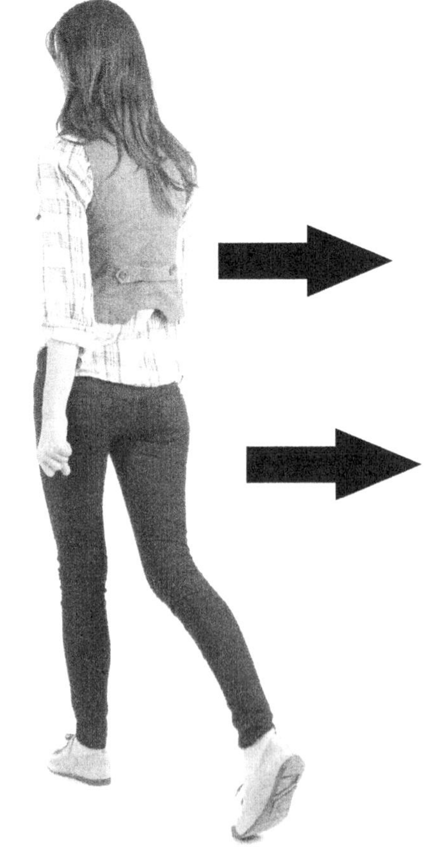

# Chapter 13
# Intensity Level

One measure of knowing how much an issue has been resolved is to begin, before tapping, by giving the issue an intensity number (IL) between 1 and 10, with 10 being high.

For example, we want a romantic partnership, yet we haven't met "the one." Thinking about a romantic relationship happening, what is the likelihood, on a scale of 1 - 10, with 10 being very likely and 1, not likely at all, of a romantic relationship happening?

Okay. We give ourselves a 2. Now, let's start tapping!

When asked what the issues might be, "Well," we say, "it does not seem as if the people who I want, want me."

Great tapping statement. Tap, "Even though the people I want don't want me, I totally and completely accept myself." After tapping, we check in with ourselves; the IL has gone up to a 4, so it is now a little bit more likely.

What comes to mind now? "No one will find me desirable." Great tapping statement. "Even though no one will find me desirable, I totally and completely accept myself." Check the IL. How likely? 5. Cool! Progress.

What comes to mind now? "I'm not comfortable being vulnerable in romantic relationships." Great tapping statement. "Even though I'm not comfortable being vulnerable in a romantic relationship, I totally and completely accept myself." Check the IL. Now it is a 6. Still progress.

What comes to mind now? "Well, it feels like if I am in a relationship, I will lose a lot of my freedom." Make this into a tapping statement. "Even though I will lose my freedom when I am in a relationship, I totally and completely accept myself." The IL has gone up to a 7.

What comes to mind now? "Oh, if I was in a relationship, I would have to be accountable to someone!" Make this into a tapping statement: "Even though, I would have to be accountable to someone if I was in a relationship, I totally and completely accept myself." Wow...the IL is 9, very likely!

Giving an issue an Intensity Level gives at the beginning and throughout the session gives us an indication of the progress we are making with resolving and/or healing that issue in our lives.

# Chapter 14
# Yawning and Taking a Deep Breath

From Traditional Chinese Medicine, we know that when chi (energy) flows freely through the meridians, the body is healthy and balanced. Physical, mental, and/or emotional illness can result when the energy is blocked.

Dysfunctional beliefs and emotions produce blocks along the meridians, blocking energy from flowing freely in the body.

With EFT Tapping, as we tap, we release the blocks. As blocked energy is able to flow more freely, the body can now "breathe a sigh of relief." Yawning is that sigh of relief.

If, after tapping, we can take a complete, deep, full, and satisfying breath, we know that an EFT Tapping statement has cleared. This yawn is an indication that an EFT Tapping statement has cleared.

If the yawn or breath is not a full, deep breath then the statement did not clear completely.

# Chapter 15
# Integration...What Happens After Tapping

After tapping, our system needs some downtime for integration to take place. When the physical body and the mind are "idle," integration can take place.

Sometimes, in the first 24 hours after tapping, we might find ourselves vegging more than normal, sleeping more than normal, or more tired than normal. This downtime is needed to integrate the new changes.

After installing a new program into our computer, sometimes we have to reboot the computer (shut down and restart) for the new program to be integrated into the system.

After tapping, our bodies need to reboot. We need some downtime. When we sleep, the new changes are integrated.

HEALING BEGINS NATURALLY AFTER THE BODY HAS HAD A CHANCE TO INTEGRATE.

Sometimes, after tapping, we forget the intensity of our pain and think that feeling better had nothing to do with tapping. Something so simple could not possibly create the improvement in our state of mind!

When we cut our finger, once it is healed, we don't even remember cutting our finger. As we move toward health, wealth, and well-being, sometimes we don't remember how unhappy, restless, or isolated we once felt.

# Chapter 16
# EFT Tapping Doesn't Work for Me

Why might EFT Tapping not be working?

* The tapping statement might not be worded such that a dysfunctional belief and/or emotion is addressed and eliminated.
* The style (laser-focused style vs round robin) of tapping may not be effective for the statement to be cleared.
* The EFT Tapping statement is only addressing a symptom and **not the cause of the issue.**

FOR EFT TAPPING TO BE EFFECTIVE, THE CAUSE OF THE ISSUE NEEDS TO BE HEALED.

* Having an awareness of our issues does not heal the dysfunctional beliefs.
* Forgiving ourselves and/or someone else does not heal the dysfunctional beliefs.
* Talk therapy does not heal the dysfunctional beliefs.
* Desensitizing the emotions does not heal the dysfunctional beliefs.
* Healing the experience of a hurtful event does not change the dysfunctional beliefs.

EFT Tapping works best when

1) the statements are worded to eliminate the dysfunctional beliefs,
2) the most effective style of tapping is utilized, and
3) we are healing the cause, not just the symptoms.

# Chapter 17
# What to Do if an EFT Tapping Statement Does Not Clear

When a statement might not clear, turn the statement into a question. The statement, "It's not okay for me to be powerful," didn't clear. **Turn the tapping statement into a question:** "Why isn't it okay for me to be powerful?"

The answer might be:

* Powerful people are ruthless and heartless.
* I am afraid of being powerful.
* Being powerful would change me for the worse.
* Power corrupts.
* People would laugh at me if I tried being powerful.
* I would have to give up my fears and anxieties to be powerful.
* I might be called aggressive if I tried being powerful.
* I do not have the abilities, skills, or qualities to be powerful.
* Others would make fun of me if I tried being powerful.
* Powerful people are thoughtless and self-centered.

With these beliefs, it might not be okay or safe to be powerful or even explore the idea of being powerful. The statements above are tapping statements. Tap the answer to the question.

After tapping the answer to the question, revisit the original statement that did not clear. Most likely, it will now be cleared, and you will be able to take a full, deep, and complete breath.

# Chapter 18
# Science and EFT Tapping Research

EFT has been researched in more than ten countries by more than sixty investigators whose results have been published in more than twenty different peer-reviewed journals. Two leading researchers are Dawson Church, Ph.D. and David Feinstein, Ph.D.

Dr. Dawson Church, a leading expert on energy psychology and an EFT master, has gathered all the research information, and it can be found on this website: www.EFTUniverse.com.

## Two Research Studies

### 1) Harvard Medical School Studies and the Brain's Stress Response

Studies at the Harvard Medical School reveal that stimulating the body's meridian points significantly reduces activity in a part of the brain called the amygdala.

The amygdala can be thought of as the body's alarm system. When the body is experiencing trauma or fear, the amygdala is triggered, and the body is flooded with cortisol, also known as the stress hormone. The stress response sets up an intricate chain reaction.

The studies showed that stimulating or tapping points along the meridians such as EFT Tapping, drastically reduced and/or eliminated the stress response and the resulting chain reaction.

### 2) Dr. Dawson Church and Cortisol Reduction

Another significant study was conducted by Dr. Dawson Church. He studied the impact an hour's tapping session had on the cortisol levels of eighty-three subjects. He also measured the cortisol levels of people who received traditional talk therapy and those of a third group who received no treatment at all.

On average, for the eighty-three subjects who completed an hour tapping session, cortisol levels were reduced by 24%. Some subjects experienced a 50% reduction in cortisol levels.

The subjects who completed one hour of traditional talk therapy and those who had completed neither session did not experience any significant cortisol reduction.

# Chapter 19
# Is Lowering the Cortisol Level Enough to Permanently Change Our Lives?

Several things can lower our cortisol (stress hormone) levels including:
* Power posing
* Meditating
* Laughing
* Exercising regularly
* Listening to music
* Getting a massage
* Eliminating caffeine from our diet
* Eating a balanced, nutritious meal and eliminating processed food

Would performing any of the above activities lower our cortisol level enough to permanently change our lives? Only if the activity eliminates the dysfunctional beliefs on a subconscious level.

All of our thoughts, feelings, actions, reactions, choices, and decisions are preceded by a belief. To change our lives, the dysfunctional beliefs must be eliminated.

Power posing, listening to music, or eating a balanced meal will not permanently change our lives. Exercising will help our physical body but will not delete our dysfunctional beliefs. Laughing will bring us into the present so we will not be drawn into our fears or anger, but it will not change our lives. Meditating helps us to center and balance, but will not change our lives on a permanent basis.

To change our lives, we must be able to recognize, acknowledge, and take ownership of that which we want to change then delete the dysfunctional emotions and beliefs that preceded that what we want to change on a subconscious level.

EFT Tapping will delete dysfunctional emotions and beliefs on a subconscious level if we provide the correct "instructions" to our subconscious mind. We must word the tapping statements in the subconscious' language. We must word the tapping statement so the subconscious mind hears what we want to eliminate.

# Chapter 20
# Tapping Affirmations

* I am healthy and happy.
* Wealth is pouring into my life.
* I radiate love and happiness.
* I have the perfect job for me.
* I am successful in whatever I do.

If we were to tap "I am healthy and happy now" and we are not, most likely, as we are tapping, we might think, "Yeah, right. Sure. I am healthy and happy. My life sucks. I hate my job. I am always broke. There is never enough money..."

The body knows this is not true. We are not healthy and happy now. When we tap, we might have difficulty remembering what we are saying, lose focus and concentration, and/or the mind drifts.

An EFT Tapping statement is most effective **when** it matches our current belief.

The subconscious does not hear the word "No." One way of tapping affirmations and, at the same time, putting in the positives is to put the word "no" into the tapping statements.

* I am **not** healthy and happy. Subconscious hears: I am healthy and happy.
* Wealth is **not** pouring into my life. Subconscious hears: Wealth is pouring into my life.
* I **do not** radiate love and happiness. Subconscious hears: I radiate love and happiness.
* I **do not** have the perfect job for me. Subconscious hears: I have the perfect job for me.
* I am **not** successful in whatever I do. Subconscious hears: I am successful in whatever I do.

If we repeat affirmations over and over and over before we clear the affirmation with EFT Tapping, repeating the affirmation numerous times will have little effect except to create circumstances in our lives so we can be confronted with the beliefs that do not align with the affirmation.

# Chapter 21
# Finishing Touches (Optional)

Some like to finish their tapping with statements that are centering and calming. If this is you, then you might want to try the 16 statements on the next page or make up those that you like. The statements can be said in any order that works for you.

| Tapping Location | Statement |
|---|---|
| Eyebrow | All is well in my life. |
| Temple | Every day in every way |
| Under the Eye | I am fulfilled in every way, every day. |
| Under the Nose | My blessings appears in rich |
| Under the Lips | I am an excellent steward of wealth and am blessed with great abundance. |
| Under the Collarbone Knob | I take complete responsibility |
| Under the Arm | I have all the tools, skills, and |
| Top back part of the Head | I know I will be able to handle anything |
| Eyebrow | All my dreams, hopes, wishes, and goals |
| Temple | Divine love expressing through me, |
| Under the Eye | I am comfortable with my life changing. |
| Under the Nose | I am able to create all that I desire. |
| Under the Lips | I know what needs to be done and |
| Under the Collarbone Knob | My health is perfect in every way, physically, |
| Under the Arm | I invite into my subconscious Archangel Raphael to heal all that needs to be forgiven, released, and redeemed. Cleanse me and free me from it now. |
| Top back part of the Head | The light of God surrounds me. The love of God enfolds me. The power of God protects me. The presence of God watches over and flows through me. |

# Chapter 22
# How to Use This Book

1. The statements are divided into sections. Read through the statements in one section. As you read a statement, notice if you have any reaction to the statement or feel the statement might be true for you. If so, note the number for that statement.

2. Once you have completed reading all the statements in one section, go back and reread the statements you noted and rate them on a scale of 1 - 10, with 10 being a "biggie."

3. List the top statements.

4. From this list, select one and describe how it plays out in your life. It is important to recognize and identify the pattern. What are the consequences of having this belief? Is there a trigger? How does it begin? How does it benefit you? How has it harmed you? There will be a different example listed in each section.

5. Tap the statements. Statements can be combined for scripts...a different statement on each of the different tapping points in one round of tapping.

6. Describe any flashbacks or memories that you might have had as you were tapping out the statements. Describe any ah-has, insights, and/or thoughts you might have had as a result of tapping the statements.

7. After tapping all the statements, review them to determine if you still have a reaction to any of the statements. If you do, you have several options. One, put a "Why" before the statement. Tap out the answer. Secondly, note that this statement may not have cleared and continue on to the next section. Most likely, after additional statements are tapped, statements that may not have cleared, will clear without having to tap the statement again.

8. Allow some downtime for integration and for the body to heal.

9. The number of sections you do at a time will be up to you. Initially, you might want to do one section to determine if you get tired and need to have some downtime after tapping.

10. The day after tapping, again review the statements you tapped to determine if you still have a reaction. If you do, follow the instructions in #7.

# EFT Tapping Statements for Non-Military PTSD 1 - 20 EFT Tapping Statements

*Let your hopes, not your hurts, shape your future.*

*Robert H. Schuller*

1. I am lost in overwhelm.
2. My life has no meaning.
3. War shattered my plans.
4. I'm stuck in survival mode.
5. I was trained to be a killer.
6. Everything feels hopeless.
7. I am detached from my life.
8. I have radial mood changes.
9. I'm unable to move forward.
10. My soul has been wounded.
11. I live a day-to-day existence.
12. I don't feel safe in the world.
13. My life stalled at the trauma.
14. The world is not a safe place.
15. I'm not able to cope with life.
16. I have shut down emotionally.
17. I expect the worse to happen.
18. My life will never be the same.
19. I have difficulty concentrating.
20. I am stupid, weak, and a failure.

# Journaling Pages for Statements 1 - 20

*Where there is pain, let there be softening.*
*Where there is bitterness, let there be acceptance.*
*Where there is despair, let there be hope...*

*Ruth Eiseman*

1. From the tapping statements between 1 - 20, list the top seven statements that you thought or felt applied to you:

1.

2.

3.

4.

5.

6.

7.

2. From this list of seven statements, select one and describe how it plays out in your life. Give an example or two. It is important to recognize and identify the pattern. Is there a trigger? How does it begin? How has it benefited you? How has it harmed you? For instance, did your life stall at the trauma? Moving forward, is it about fear? Not knowing who you are now that the trauma has happened? Not having any goals to move forward towards?

3. Tap out the top 7 statements.

4. As you were tapping out the statements, did you have any flashback or memories of the past, any additional insights, and/or ah-ha thoughts? If so, write them down. Make note of them.

# EFT Tapping Statements for Military PTSD
# 21 - 40 EFT Tapping Statements

*Every adversity, every failure, every heartache carries with it the seed of an equal or greater benefit.*

*Napoleon Hill*

21. My rage frightens those around me.
22. There is no reason to keep on living.
23. My self-esteem has been destroyed.
24. I use alcohol to numb the memories.
25. The world is a very dangerous place.
26. I am full of self-doubt and insecurity.
27. My self-confidence has been eroded.
28. The world is a very threatening place.
29. I am cynical and mistrusting of others.
30. I was trained to hate and dehumanize.
31. I don't take care of my physical health.
32. I can't get beyond my disappointment.
33. I am not able to move beyond survival.
34. I have difficulty participating in my life.
35. I have difficulty finding meaning to life.
36. The inner restlessness is ever ongoing.
37. I am powerless to create the life I want.
38. I don't have the tools and skills to thrive.
39. I never thought I would see home again.
40. I stuff and suppress my anxious feelings.

# Journaling Pages for Statements 21 - 40

*Peace is not the absence of violence but*
*the manifestation of human compassion.*

*Dalai Lama*

1. From the tapping statements between 1 - 20, list the top seven statements that you thought or felt applied to you:

1.

2.

3.

4.

5.

6.

7.

2. From this list of seven statements, select one and describe how it plays out in your life. Give an example or two. It is important to recognize and identify the pattern. Is there a trigger? How does it begin? How has it benefited you? How has it harmed you? For instance, are you preoccupied with thoughts of death and suicide? Sometimes when we are caught in survival, we just want to stop the endless cycle of fear, anxiety, anguish, depression, and anger. When everything seems hopeless, we think of suicide. The solution is to desensitize and heal the dysfunctional emotions.

3. Tap out the top 7 statements.

4. As you were tapping out the statements, did you have any flashback or memories of the past, any additional insights, and/or ah-ha thoughts? If so, write them down. Make note of them.

# EFT Tapping Statements for Survival
# 41 – 60 EFT Tapping Statements

*The truth is that our finest moments are most likely to occur when we are feeling deeply uncomfortable, unhappy, or unfulfilled. For it is only in such moments, propelled by our discomfort, that we are likely to step out of our ruts and start searching for different ways or truer answers.*

*M. Scott Peck*

41. I feel lost, confused, and afraid.
42. War robbed me of a joyous life.
43. I am drowning in my depression.
44. I feel defeated and demoralized.
45. I feel inadequate in living my life.
46. My life has been altered forever.
47. I have withdrawn from the world.
48. I've become numb to everything.
49. Feeling feelings is overwhelming.
50. I have difficulty making decisions.
51. My communication skills are poor.
52. I am awkward at social gatherings.
53. Life is filled with pitfalls and perils.
54. There is nothing special about me.
55. It's not safe to step into my power.
56. I can't handle the difficulties of life.
57. I am always on the alert for danger.
58. My life lacks direction and purpose.
59. I feel angry, frustrated, and hateful.
60. I feel sad, rejected, and abandoned.

# Journaling Pages for Statements 41 - 60

*If you are going through hell, keep going.*

*Rob Estes*

1. From the tapping statements between 1 - 20, list the top seven statements that you thought or felt applied to you:

1.

2.

3.

4.

5.

6.

7.

2. From this list of seven statements, select one and describe how it plays out in your life. Give an example or two. It is important to recognize and identify the pattern. Is there a trigger? How does it begin? How has it benefited you? How has it harmed you? For instance, are you stuck at disappointment? Are you now not moving forward to avoid disappointment? Are you desiring and waiting for a guarantee that nothing bad will happen again? Is it safer to stagnate?

3. Tap out the top 7 statements.

4. As you were tapping out the statements, did you have any flashback or memories of the past, any additional insights, and/or ah-ha thoughts? If so, write them down. Make note of them.

# 61 – 80 EFT Tapping Statements

*Ships are safe in the harbor, but that's not what ships are for.*

*William Shedd*

61. I am cold, aloof, uncaring, and detached.
62. I am terrified and near panic all the time.
63. I have difficulty expressing my emotions.
64. My trauma has limited who I can become.
65. I can't share with anyone the agony I feel.
66. I'm having difficulty adjusting to civilian life.
67. I overindulge in alcohol, drugs, and/or food.
68. I am paralyzed and unable to move forward.
69. Others see me as defective, flawed, and bad.
70. Stability and feeling secure are out of reach.
71. My life is about pain, struggle, and suffering.
72. I don't know how to move out of the rat race.
73. I constantly worry about what might happen.
74. I am powerless to live my life any differently.
75. I am overwhelmed with the task of surviving.
76. It is not okay/safe to move forward in my life.
77. My life lacks meaning, purpose, and direction.
78. I am super-sensitive to criticism and rejection.
79. I never allow anyone to really get to know me.
80. I don't have what it takes to cope with my life.

# Journaling Pages for Statements 61 - 80

*Man cannot discover new oceans unless*
*he has courage to lose sight of the shore.*

*Andre Gide*

1. From the tapping statements between 1 - 20, list the top seven statements that you thought or felt applied to you:

1.

2.

3.

4.

5.

6.

7.

2. From this list of seven statements, select one and describe how it plays out in your life. Give an example or two. It is important to recognize and identify the pattern. Is there a trigger? How does it begin? How has it benefited you? How has it harmed you? For instance, are you caught in survival? Have you been in survival for so long that you don't know who you would be when you are not in survival mode? Is your identify that of always being in survival, crisis mode? What would be the consequences of changing your identify, of removing the mask?

3. Tap out the top 7 statements.

4. As you were tapping out the statements, did you have any flashback or memories of the past, any additional insights, and/or ah-ha thoughts? If so, write them down. Make note of them.

# 81 - 100 EFT Tapping Statements

*People are like guided missiles. Without a target, they wander aimlessly across the horizons and eventually self-destruct.*

*Edge Keynote*

81. I am broken beyond repair.
82. I am inferior to other people.
83. I am paralyzed by my trauma.
84. I second guess everything I do.
85. I doubt my abilities and talents.
86. I'm too insecure to be powerful.
87. I don't feel at home in the world.
88. Power is mean, cruel, and hurtful.
89. I cannot transcend my limitations.
90. I am too fearful to be empowered.
91. I chose defeat over determination.
92. I constantly feel tired and fatigued.
93. I have difficulty making decisions.
94. I am too insecure to be empowered.
95. I feel sad, worthless, and depressed.
96. I am not important and don't matter.
97. I expect the worst to always happen.
98. It is not safe to think outside the box.
99. I am full of self-doubt and insecurity.
100. I am critical of myself and my actions.

# Journaling Pages for Statements 81 - 100

*Your biggest problem or difficulty today has been sent to you at this moment to teach you something you need to know to be happier and more successful in the future.*

*Brian Tracy*

1. From the tapping statements between 1 - 20, list the top seven statements that you thought or felt applied to you:

1.

2.

3.

4.

5.

6.

7.

2. From this list of seven statements, select one and describe how it plays out in your life. Give an example or two. It is important to recognize and identify the pattern. Is there a trigger? How does it begin? How has it benefited you? How has it harmed you? For instance, do you have difficulty making decisions? If so, is this because you never learned how to make decisions, you don't trust your ability to make decisions, or because you would have to take action on the decisions you make?

3. Tap out the top 7 statements.

4. As you were tapping out the statements, did you have any flashback or memories of the past, any additional insights, and/or ah-ha thoughts? If so, write them down. Make note of them.

# 101 - 120 EFT Tapping Statements

*It is not who we are that holds us back. It is who we think we are not.*

*Michael Nolan*

101. I feel defeated, beaten, and bankrupt.
102. I am too depressed to be empowered.
103. I second-guess every decision I make.
104. I lack the self worth to be empowered.
105. I am powerless to create the life I want.
106. I lack the confidence to be empowered.
107. I feel defenseless, weak, and vulnerable.
108. I don't know how to step into my power.
109. I feel inadequate, unworthy, and inferior.
110. I am powerless to move beyond my pain.
111. I am too self destructive to be empowered.
112. My self-talk is more negative than positive.
113. Others see me as defective, flawed, and bad.
114. There is something basically wrong with me.
115. I am not able to step out of my comfort zone.
116. I don't have the skills needed to be powerful.
117. I cannot deal with the challenges of daily life.
118. Yesterday takes up too much of my thoughts.
119. I'm not willing to step up to the plate and bat.
120. Being empowered is stressful and exhausting.

# Journaling Pages for Statements 101 - 120

*Trust, integrity, and gratitude, these are the foundation upon which we should build our lives. If we learn to trust ourselves, we will know truth. If we are honest with ourselves, we will know integrity. If we are thankful for all that is, we will know love.*

*Tessa Cason*

1. From the tapping statements between 1 - 20, list the top seven statements that you thought or felt applied to you:

1.

2.

3.

4.

5.

6.

7.

2. From this list of seven statements, select one and describe how it plays out in your life. Give an example or two. It is important to recognize and identify the pattern. Is there a trigger? How does it begin? How has it benefited you? How has it harmed you? For instance, do you feel painful memories will be with you forever? Every life experience can teach us something to be more successful in the future. What life lessons are you learning by being disempowered?

3. Tap out the top 7 statements.

4. As you were tapping out the statements, did you have any flashback or memories of the past, any additional insights, and/or ah-ha thoughts? If so, write them down. Make note of them.

# 121 – 140 EFT Tapping Statements

*Courage is not the absence of fear, rather the judgment that something else is more important than fear.*

*Ambrose Redmoon*

121. I am full of self-doubt.
122. I am paralyzed by fear.
123. I will never master my fears.
124. I expect the worse to happen.
125. Fear fuels my need to control.
126. I lack supportive relationships.
127. I am anxious about everything.
128. The world is a hazardous place.
129. Fear is my constant companion.
130. I avoid confrontation at all cost.
131. "Just do it" doesn't work for me.
132. I have a constant sense of doom.
133. I didn't expect life to be so hard.
134. I can't stop the negative self-talk.
135. I'm not able to conquer my fears.
136. I am not free to explore the world.
137. I avoid any and all confrontations.
138. I allow fear to limit my possibilities.
139. Life is frightening and intimidating.
140. I know I am weak and incompetent.

# Journaling Pages for Statements 121 - 140

*Fear stifles our thinking and actions. It creates indecisiveness that results in stagnation.*

*Charles Stanley*

1. From the tapping statements between 1 - 20, list the top seven statements that you thought or felt applied to you:

1.

2.

3.

4.

5.

6.

7.

2. From this list of seven statements, select one and describe how it plays out in your life. Give an example or two. It is important to recognize and identify the pattern. Is there a trigger? How does it begin? How has it benefited you? How has it harmed you? For instance, is it safe to let your fears go? If not, what are your fears keeping you safe from? Moving forward? Having a relationship? Being responsible? What are you avoiding and how is your fear keeping you safe from that which you are avoiding?

3. Tap out the top 7 statements.

4. As you were tapping out the statements, did you have any flashback or memories of the past, any additional insights, and/or ah-ha thoughts? If so, write them down. Make note of them.

# 141 – 160 EFT Tapping Statements

*There comes a time when the risk to remain tight in a bud will be more painful than the risk it takes to blossom.*

*Anais Nin*

141. I feel nervous, helpless, and fearful.
142. The world is not a safe place to live.
143. I feel resentful, powerless, and angry.
144. My life has been turned upside down.
145. I feel defeated, hopeless, and trapped.
146. I agonized over every decision I make.
147. Fear is the noose that is strangling me.
148. I am a prisoner of my own insecurities.
149. I never learned coping skills as a child.
150. Fear is a major stumbling block for me.
151. I have a lot of doubt and indecisiveness.
152. I allow my fears to restrict my activities.
153. I am sinking in the quicksand of despair.
154. My life is stagnant as a result of my fears.
155. I don't have the confidence to be fearless.
156. I will not venture out of my comfort zone.
157. The word courage is not in my vocabulary.
158. I will never be able to move through the fear.
159. I feel overwhelmed, defeated, and victimized.
160. Being a coward is a cover for my incompetence.

# Journaling Pages for Statements 141 - 160

*Fear is static that prevents us from hearing ourselves.*

*Samuel Butler*

1. From the tapping statements between 1 - 20, list the top seven statements that you thought or felt applied to you:

1.

2.

3.

4.

5.

6.

7.

2. From this list of seven statements, select one and describe how it plays out in your life. Give an example or two. It is important to recognize and identify the pattern. Is there a trigger? How does it begin? How has it benefited you? How has it harmed you? For instance, are you in charge of your life? If not you, then who? Your anger? Your fear? Neither of these provide us with an accurate assessment. FEAR - False Evidence Appearing Real!

3. Tap out the top 7 statements.

4. As you were tapping out the statements, did you have any flashback or memories of the past, any additional insights, and/or ah-ha thoughts? If so, write them down. Make note of them.

# 161 – 180 EFT Tapping Statements

*At the core of all anger is a need that is not being fulfilled.*

*Marshall B. Rosenberg*

161. I am my harshest critic.
162. Inner peace is an illusion.
163. The world is a hostile place.
164. I act in ugly and mean ways.
165. I am a slave to my own anger.
166. I seem to be angry all the time.
167. My anger comes on really fast.
168. I get angry when I feel insecure.
169. Life is unfair, abusive, and cruel.
170. I am full of anger, rage, and hate.
171. I feel angry, sad, hurt, and lonely.
172. Criticism bothers me a great deal.
173. I suppress my anger and hostility.
174. Life is one problem after another.
175. My anger catches me by surprise.
176. I am condemning and judgmental.
177. The only emotion I know is anger.
178. My anger is explosive and sudden.
179. The world is full of hate and scorn.
180. I have intense conflicts with others.

# Journaling Pages for Statements 161 - 180

*Anger are the tears we don't allow ourselves to shed; ones that we feel we might not have a right to or others would think us weak for shedding.*

*Tessa Cason*

1. From the tapping statements between 1 - 20, list the top seven statements that you thought or felt applied to you:

1.

2.

3.

4.

5.

6.

7.

2. From this list of seven statements, select one and describe how it plays out in your life. Give an example or two. It is important to recognize and identify the pattern. Is there a trigger? How does it begin? How has it benefited you? How has it harmed you? For instance, do you feel guilty after you blow up in anger? Guilt is anger we don't feel we have a right to have. Anger is not bad or good, right or wrong. It just is. It's the expression of the anger, when it harms another person that makes it wrong and destructive. Why is it not okay for you to have the anger you feel? How can you heal your anger without harming someone else?

3. Tap out the top 7 statements.

4. As you were tapping out the statements, did you have any flashback or memories of the past, any additional insights, and/or ah-ha thoughts? If so, write them down. Make note of them.

# 181 – 200 EFT Tapping Statements

*No man can think clearly when his fists are clenched.*

*George Jean* Nathan

181. I shout at anyone that criticizes me.
182. I'm angry that this happened to me.
183. My anger is too powerful to control.
184. I lose total control when I get angry.
185. I judge others and/or myself harshly.
186. I hang onto my anger for a long time.
187. I'm too gullible when I am optimistic.
188. My thoughts are clouded by my anger.
189. I am always on guard to defend myself.
190. My anger destroys all my relationships.
191. My anger is volatile and uncontrollable.
192. I am quiet and passive when I am angry.
193. I do destructive things when I am angry.
194. I use anger to push people out of my life.
195. I yell back at people that are angry at me.
196. I am angry at other people's insensitivity.
197. I get very angry when people criticize me.
198. I am easily provoked and short-tempered.
199. I use the silent treatment when I am angry.
200. I use anger to avoid other issues in my life.

# Journaling Pages for Statements 181 - 200

*Fear is the path to the dark side. Fear leads to anger.*
*Anger leads to hate. Hate leads to suffering.*

*Yoda*

1. From the tapping statements between 1 - 20, list the top seven statements that you thought or felt applied to you:

1.

2.

3.

4.

5.

6.

7.

2. From this list of seven statements, select one and describe how it plays out in your life. Give an example or two. It is important to recognize and identify the pattern. Is there a trigger? How does it begin? How has it benefited you? How has it harmed you? For instance, are you angry for what you have lost? Are you angry that you are stuck? Are you angry that your life is not what you thought it would be? Are you angry that you are only surviving and not thriving?

3. Tap out the top 7 statements.

4. As you were tapping out the statements, did you have any flashback or memories of the past, any additional insights, and/or ah-ha thoughts? If so, write them down. Make note of them.

# Books by Tessa Cason

## All Things EFT Tapping Manual

* Why does EFT Tapping work for some and not for others?
* How do you personalize EFT Tapping to be most effective for you?
* What is the very first tapping statement you need to tap?

This manual provides instructions on how to heal our disappointments, regrets, and painful memories.

EFT Tapping information has instructions on what to do if a tapping statement does not clear, what to do if tapping doesn't work for you, and how to write your own tapping statements.

We must eliminate the dysfunctional beliefs if we want to make changes in our lives. EFT Tapping can do just that. EFT Tapping is a simple, yet very powerful tool to heal our beliefs, emotions, painful memories, and stories.

## 500 EFT Tapping Statements for Moving Out of Survival

Survival is stress on steroids. It's feeling anxious and not good enough. Survival may be the most important topic we can heal within ourselves. Survival is programmed into our DNA.

Ella returned home from the market with her three year old daughter to find a note from her husband that he did not want to be married any longer. Under the note were divorce papers, the number of the divorce attorney, and $500.

Wanting to be able to give her daughter a wonderful childhood, she had to figure out how to survive and thrive. This is her story and the tapping statements she tapped.

Dr. John Montgomery says, "All 'negative,' or distressing, emotions, like fear, disgust, or anxiety, can be thought of as 'survival-mode' emotions: they signal that our survival and well-being may be at risk."

## 80 EFT Tapping Statements for Change

If it is not okay or safe for our lives to change, every time our lives change, the body is subjected to a tremendous amount of stress.

After graduating from high school, Charlie's dad told Charlie he could continue to live at home, but he would be charged room and board. At 18, Charlie was now financially responsible for himself. He was able to find a job and moved out.

Within a year, circumstances forced Charlie to move back home. Day after day, Charlie rode the bus to work. After work, he rode the bus home. One day as Charlie was riding the bus to work, he noticed another regular rider, Dan, tapping his head.

Together Dan and Charlie began tapping. Find out the results of their tapping and the statements they tapped.

## 300 EFT Tapping Statements for Self-defeating Behaviors, Victim, Self-pity

Tom had lots of excuses and reasons for his lack of "results." His boss, Robert MacGregor, saw the potential Tom had and asked his longtime friend, Sam Anderson, a life coach, to work with Tom. Read Tom's story to understand how Tom was able to step into his potential.

Self defeating behaviors take us away from our goals, from what we want, leaving us feeling exhausted, disempowered, and defeated. Self defeating thoughts are the negative thoughts we have about ourselves and/or the world around us such as "I'm not good enough", "I have to be perfect to be accepted."

Most likely, you have tried to change the self-defeating and self sabotage behavior, yet here you are with the same patterns.

## 100 EFT Tapping Statements for Feeling Fulfilled

John wasn't sure what would fulfill him. He loved his job and didn't want to find a new career, but he wasn't feeling fulfilled in his life. With the help of his wife, John found what would be fulfilling.

Fulfillment is a simple formula, actually. It's the follow-through that might be the problem.

What would prevent you from being fulfilled? Do you know what the blocks might be, the reason you remain out of sync, unfulfilled? Is it about leaving your comfort zone or maybe it's that you allow your limitations to define your life?

It is possible to remove the blocks, heal the beliefs on the subconscious level, and move toward your desire for fulfillment. To do so, we need a powerful tool. One such tool is EFT Tapping, the Emotional Freedom Technique.

Being Extraordinary

100 EFT Tapping Statements™ for Being Extraordinary! Tessa Cason

## 100 EFT Tapping Statements for Being Extraordinary!

Accomplishing extraordinary performances, having incredible successes, or earning large sums of money does not equate to an extraordinary person. This book is about discovering your extraordinary character.

Extraordinary - Exceeding ordinary, beyond ordinary.

Extraordinary starts with the self, our character, depth and strength of our being. It's being congruent, walking our talk. It is the love, compassion, and tenderness we show ourselves. It's the pure and highest essence of our being.

Rebecca was approaching a time in her life in which she was doing some soul searching and examining her life. She didn't feel extraordinary. In her late 50s, she felt she was just ordinary. She reached out to Tessa. The email exchanges are included in this book along with tapping statements.

## 400 EFT Tapping Statements for Being Empowered and Successful

Being empowered is not about brute strength or the height of our successes. It is the strength, substance, and character of our inner being. It is knowing that whatever life throws at us, we will prevail.

Ava has just started a business with her two very successful sisters. She wants the business with her sisters to succeed, yet, she doesn't feel empowered. She doesn't want to feel as if the business would fail because of her and is ready to do the emotional work so she matches her sisters' power and success.

Sophie, Ava's roommate and an EFT practitioner-in-training, works with Ava. With Sophie's help, Ava begins to feel empowered and that her business with her sisters will be a success.

## 300 EFT Tapping Statement for Healing the Self

We live in a complex world wi multiple influences. At birth, i starts with our parents and soo afterwards, the influence of oth family members (grandparents siblings, etc.), TV shows, cartoc characters, commercials, anc peers. As we get older, we have the influences o teachers, coaches, tutors, television and movie star pop stars, sports heroes, and so many other.

When Pete was offered a promotion at work and wa not excited about something he had worked so hard t accomplish, he knew he needed to find some answe He thought he was living his mother's version of his life. He didn't know what brought him joy.

With the help of EFT and an EFT Practitioner, Pete wa able to discover his version of his life, what brough him joy, and how to live a fulfilling life.

## EFT Tapping for Anxiety, Fear, Anger, Self Pity, Courage (1,000 Tapping Statements)

Anxiety is a combination of 4 things: Unidentified Anger, Hurt, Fear, and Self Pity. We expect error, rejection, humiliation, and actually start to anticipate it.

When we are not in present time, we are either in the past or the future. Anger is the past. Fear is the future. Fear could actually be anger that we failed in the past and most likely will fail again in the future.

It takes courage on our part to heal the anxiety, identify the hurt, and to give up the self-pity. To heal, to thrive, and flourish, we need to address not only the Anxiety, but also the fear, anger, self pity, and hurt.

Healing is not about managing symptoms. It's about alleviating the cause of the symptoms.

## 80 EFT Tapping Statements for Feeling Less Than and Anxiety

Rene was excited for the year long mentoring program she enrolled in. *How wonderful,* she thought, *to be surrounded with like-minded people.* Five months into the program, she abruptly dropped out. Find out how her feeling Less Than and her Anxiety sabotaged her personal growth.

Anxiety has four parts: unidentified anger, hurt, fear, and self-pity. Living in a state of fear, we want a guarantee that our decisions and choices will produce the results or outcomes that we want. Feeling less than is played out in a cycle of shame, hopelessness, and self-pity. We feel shame about who we are, that we have little value, and that we are not good enough.

Feeling "less than" spirals down into depression, survival, and self-sabotage.

## 240 EFT Tapping Statements for Fear

Two months before school ended, Lennie was downsized from as a high school music teacher. When he was unable to find another job, fear crept into his thoughts. What if he couldn't find a job in music again? He wasn't qualified to do anything different. He was scared that he would not be able to support his family and they would end up homeless. He could feel the fear as his stomach was in knots.

Fear is that sense of dread, knots in the stomach, chill that runs down our spine, and the inability to breathe. We all know it. Fight-Flight-Freeze.

Fear is a self-protection mechanism. It is an internal alarm system that alerts us to potential harm. When we are in present time, we have the courage, awareness, wisdom, discernment, and confidence to identify and handle that which could cause us harm.

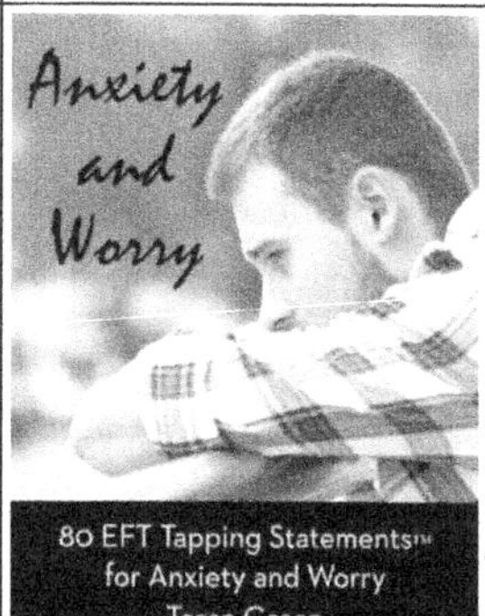


## 80 EFT Tapping Statements for Anxiety and Worry

"I just can't do this anymore," said Frank to his wife Mary. "You worry about everything. When we got married, your anxiety was something you did every now and then. But now you are paranoid about everything. I leave for work and you act like you are never going to see me again."

Anxiety is a combination of 4 things: unidentified anger, hurt, fear, self-pity. We expect error, rejection, humiliation, and actually start to anticipate it. It is an internal response to a perceived threat to our well-being. We feel threatened by an abstract, unknown danger that could harm us in the future.

Worry is a mild form of anxiety. Worry is a tendency to mull over and over and over anxiety-provoking thoughts. Worry is thinking, in an obsessive way, about something that has happened or will happen. Going over something again and again and asking, "What will I do? What should I have done?"

Healing a Broken Heart

200 EFT Tapping Statements™ for Healing a Broken Heart Tessa Cason

## 200 ET Tapping Statements for Healing a Broken Heart

She found someone who made her feel cherished, valued, and loved. Tall, dark, and handsome as well as aware, present and understanding. Matt was an awesome guy. He thought she, too, was someone special, intriguing, and awesome.

Matt was promoted at work which meant months away from home and thus, decided to end their relationship. Her best friend introduced her to EFT Tapping to heal her broken heart.

Time does not heal all. Healing the grief of a broken heart is not easy. Grief is more than sadness. Grief is a loss. Something of value is gone. Grief is an intense loss that breaks our hearts.

Over time, unhealed grief becomes anger, blame, resentment, and/or remorse. To heal a broken heart, we need to identify, acknowledge, and healed the dysfunctional beliefs. EFT Tapping can help.

## 400 EFT Tapping Statements for Dealing with Emotions

Did you see the movie Pleasantville with Tobey Maguire and Reese Witherspoon, two siblings who are trapped in a 1950s black and white TV show, set in a small midwest town where everything is seemingly perfect. David and Jennifer (Tobey and Reese) must pretend they are Bud and Mary Sue Parker, the son and daughter in the TV show.

Slowly, the town begins changing from black and white to color as the townspeople begin to experience emotions. Experiencing emotions is like adding color to a black and white movie. Color adds a depth, enjoyment, and pleasure to the movie. Emotions add depth, enjoyment, and pleasure to our lives.

Emotions add animation, richness, and warmth to our lives. They give our lives meaning and fullness. Withou emotions, our lives would be as boring as watching a black and white movie.

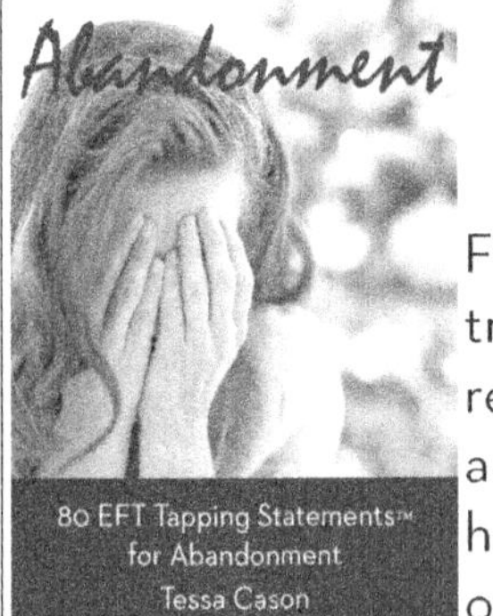


## 80 EFT Tapping Statements for Abandonment

Feelings of abandonment can be triggered by the ending of a relationship as well as the death of an individual. Even though we may have an intellectual understanding of death, there is still a feeling of abandonment when someone we treasure dies. For a small child, they do not understand death. They may still expect the parent to return at any time.

Even though Kevin drove an expensive sports car he wasn't the playboy type. He wanted to settle down and start a family. Kevin felt Susan could be "the one." He wanted to talk to her about taking their relationship to the next level.

Before Kevin could talk to Susan, she ended the relationship because of his insecurities in their relationship. She felt it had to do with the abandonment of his mom when he was a child. This book gives you the exact statements that Kevin tapped to deal with his insecurities in relationships.

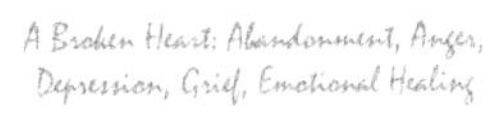

EFT Tapping Statements for A Broken Heart: Abandonment, Anger, Depression, Grief, Emotional Healing Tessa Cason

## EFT Tapping Statements for A Broken Heart: Abandonment, Anger, Depression, Grief, Emotional Healing (1,000 Statement

Time does not heal all. When our hearts have been shattered, we fee nothing will ever be the same agair We are flooded with emotions. anger, grief, depression...

Regardless of what led to the broken heart, maybe a death, divorce, or a breakup, the result is the same...a broken heart. To heal a broken heart is not only abou healing the grief, but also the feelings of abandonment anger, and depression.

Being abandoned is a verb. It is something that "happens to us." The result of being abandoned is anger, grief, and depression. Grief is the sadness we experience when we have lost something of value.

In order to heal, we need to resolve the anger, grief, abandonment, and depression that resulted from our hearts being fractured.

## 200 EFT Tapping Statements for Wealth

After graduating from high school, Amy looked for a job for a solid year unsuccessfully! She lacked the necessary experience and education. She felt like she was in a vicious cycle, going round and round and round. Finally, she was hired at a large chain store. For the last eight years, she has been shuffled, unhappily, between different departments.

As a birthday gift, her mom gave her a session with an EFT Practitioner to determine what she wanted to do with her life. Follow along with Amy on her journey to self-discovery.

What we manifest in our lives is a direct result of our beliefs. If we have a mentality of wealth and abundance, we will prosper and thrive.

Our beliefs determine the level of our wealth and abundance. To heal our dysfunctional beliefs, we need a powerful tool. EFT Tapping is one such tool.

EFT Tapping Statements for Prosperity, Survival, Courage, Personal Power, Success
Tessa Cason

## EFT Tapping Statements for Prosperity, Survival, Courage, Personal Power, Success

(1,000 Statements)

What we believe determines our prosperity. Our beliefs determine our thoughts and feelings which in turn determine our choices and decisions. Therefore, what we manifest in our lives is a direct result of our beliefs. If we are happy and joyful, we will see happiness in everything. If we are fearful, we will see fear around every corner. If we have a mentality of abundance, we will prosper.

It is difficult to be prosperous when we are stuck in survival. In survival, we feel disempowered to thrive. We can only survive. It takes Courage to step into our Personal Power and to Succeed. We need a powerful tool to heal our dysfunctional beliefs. EFT Tapping is one such tool.

In this book, there are 200 tapping statements for each of these 5 topics - Prosperity, Survival, Courage, Personal Power, and Success.

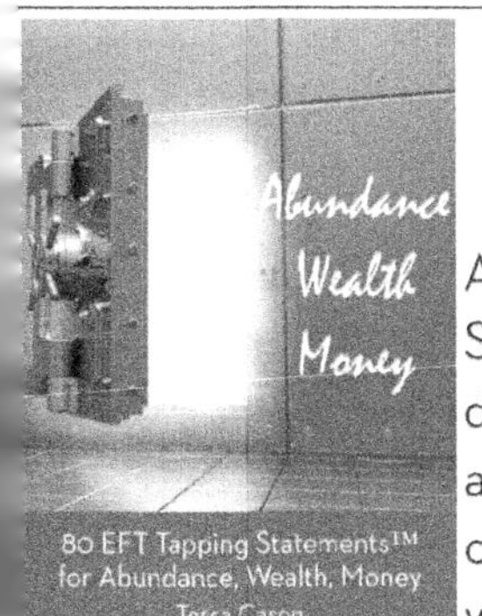


## 80 EFT Tapping Statements for Abundance, Wealth, Money

Abby just had her 46th birthday. She tried to celebrate but she didn't have anything to be happy about. Her parents had died in a car accident the Christmas before while driving home from her new home after celebrating Christmas. Both of her parents were real estate agents. She was their transaction coordinator. The three of them had their own offices, handling any real estate transaction that someone might need. Without them, she had no real estate transactions to coordinate.

Abby funds were running dry. She had applied for jobs without success. Abby talked to every one she and her parents knew in hopes of finding a job. With the slow real estate market, she was unable to find any work.

Find out how Abby turned her life around and the exact statements that Abby tapped to deal with her monetary issues.

## 400 EFT Tapping Statements for Dreams to Reality

Have you done everything you were supposed to do for your dreams to become reality? You were clear on what they were. You made your vision boards with lots of pictures of what you desired. You visualized them coming true and living that life. You've stated your affirmations over and over and over for their fulfillment. You released and allowed the Universe to handle the details. And, now, dust is collecting on your vision boards and you are still waiting for the Universe to handle the details.

Our dreams are our hopes and desires of what we want to come true one day. They are snapshots of what we want our future to be. Yet, sometimes, maybe most of the time, our dreams do not become reality and never manifest themselves in our lives. We gave up on our dreams a long time ago.

Jane shares her story of how she used EFT Tapping to turn her dreams into reality.

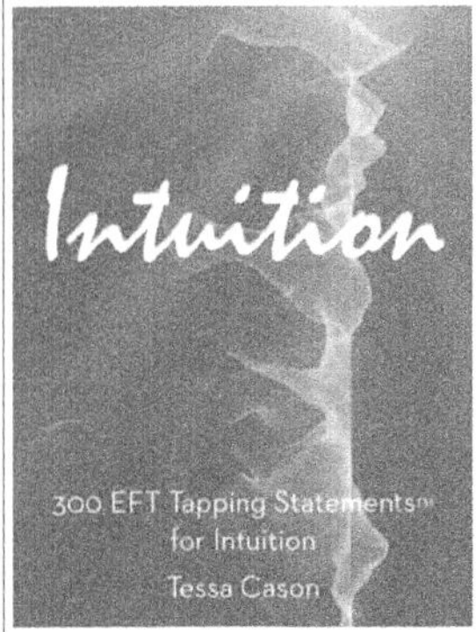


## 300 EFT Tapping Statements for Intuition

Quinn was one of Tessa's students in her Developing Your Intuition class. She had been hesitant to develop her intuition. One of her basic needs was Belonging. If she was intuitive, she might not belong and thus, realized this was part of her hesitation.

She also had a tendency to avoid which also wasn't conductive to developing her intuition. Tessa wrote out some EFT Tapping statements for her to tap:
* I ignore my inner voice.
* No one I know uses intuition.
* I'm too logical to be intuitive.
* Being intuitive is too complicated.

Included in this book are exercises and helpful hints to develop your intuition as well info on Symbolism, Colors, Number, Charkas, Asking Questions of Our Intuition, Archetypes, and 36 Possible Reasons We Took Physical Form.

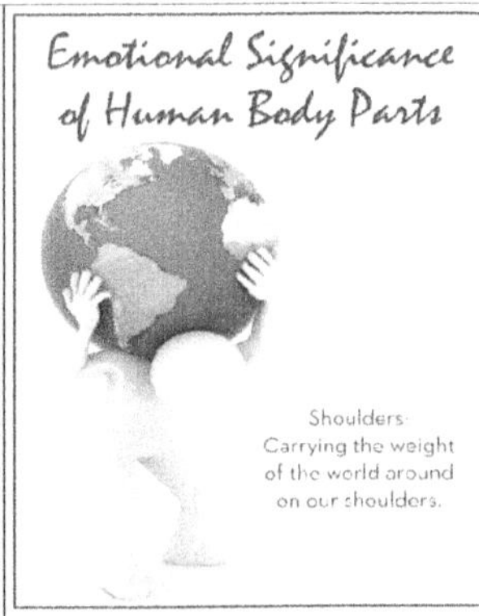


## Emotional Significance of Human Body Parts.Chasing the Pain

"We carry the weight of the world around on our shoulders." The emotional significance of the shoulder is about responsibility.

The body "talks" to us...in its language. To understand what the body is saying, we need to learn the body's language.

Jona greeted me at the airport gate on crutches. After hugging each other, she asked what the left ankle meant. I told her the left side of the body had to do with what's going on in the inside and the ankles had to do with commitments.

She had been dating a man for the last two months and he just proposed.

Chasing the Pain is a technique with EFT Tapping that as we tap for a physical pain we are experiencing, the original pain might disappear only to be felt in a different part of the body.

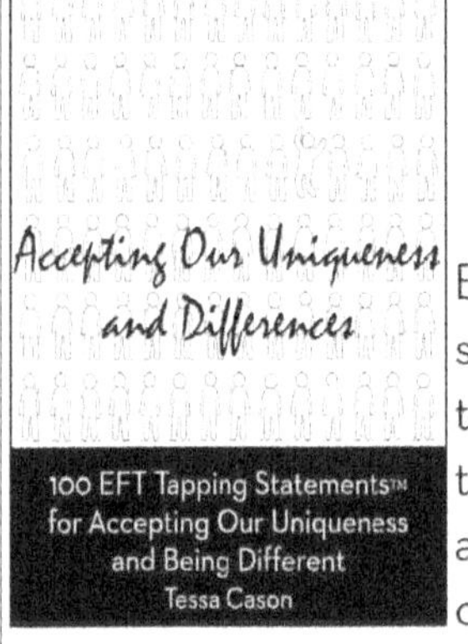


## 100 EFT Tapping Statements for Accepting Our Uniqueness and Being Different

Brian was an intelligent high school student with average grades. He tested high on all the assessment tests. Brian didn't think of himself as intelligent since his grades were only average. He didn't plan on going to college because he thought he wasn't smart enough and would flunk out.

His counselor knew otherwise and suggested Brian retake the tests to see if the tests were wrong. Find out Brian's scores after he retook the tests and how Mr. Cole introduced EFT Tapping to Brian.

If you were your unique self, do you fear being alone, rejected, or labeled as "undesirable?" Or maybe it's being laughed at and ridiculed for being different and unique?

When we play our lives safe, we end up feeling angry, anxious, powerless, hopeless, and depressed.

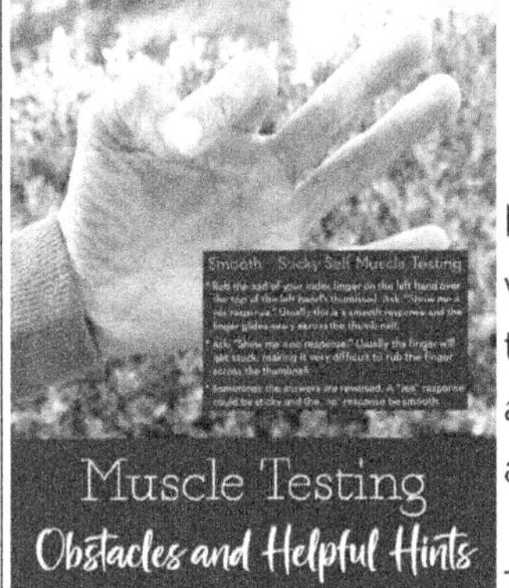


## Muscle Testing.Obstacles and Helpful Hints

Muscle testing is a method in which we can converse with the subconscious mind as well as the body's nervous system and energy field.

This book details 10 obstacles and 10 helpful hints to successfully muscle test.

One obstacle is that it is a necessity that the tester be someone that calibrates the same, or above, that of the testee, on David Hawkins' Map of Consciousness or be in the higher altitudes, 250 or higher, on the Map.

Helpful hint: When muscle testing, the tester and testee should not make eye contact with each other. With eye contact, the answer would be "our" energy instead of the "testee's" energy.

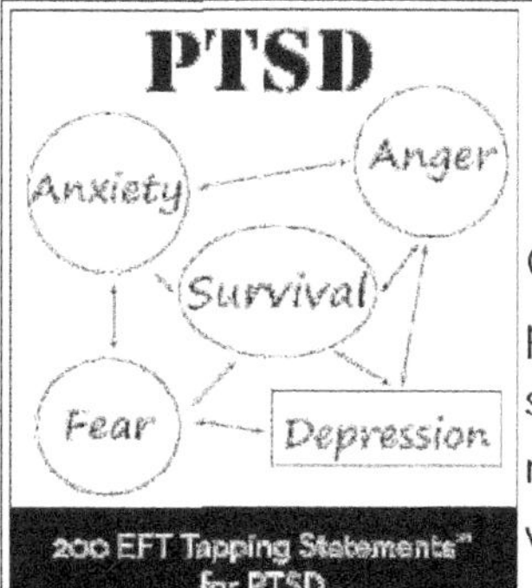


## 200 ET Tapping Statements for PTSD

George believed that if he prepared for his death, it was signaling the Universe he was ready to die. George did die without preparing his wife.

George took care of everything. The only thing Helen had to take care of George.

After George died, she had no idea if they owned the home they lived in, if George had life insurance, how to pay bills, if they had money, if they did, where was it? She didn't know if George had left a will. She was not prepared for George's death or how to take care of everything that George took care of.

With the help of friends and EFT Tapping, Helen was able to heal and learn how to take care of everything that George once did.

Healing is not about managing symptoms. It is about alleviating the cause of the symptoms.

## EFT Tapping Statements for PTSD, Survival, Disempowered, Fear, Anger (1,200 Statements)

The potential exists for anyone that is in any life threatening situation in which they fear for their life, that believes death is imminent, to experience PTSD.

With PTSD, our Survival is at stake. As a result of our survival being threatened, we feel Disempowered to thrive. We can only survive. When we are caught in Survival, Fear is a prevalent emotion. When we feel Disempowered, Anger is just beneath the surface.

To heal, to thrive, and flourish, we need to address not only the PTSD, but also Survival and Feeling Disempowered, Fear, and Anger. (Thus, the 5 topics in this PTSD Workbook.)

Healing PTSD is a process in which we must desensitize, decrease, and heal the survival response. EFT Tapping is the best method to do so.

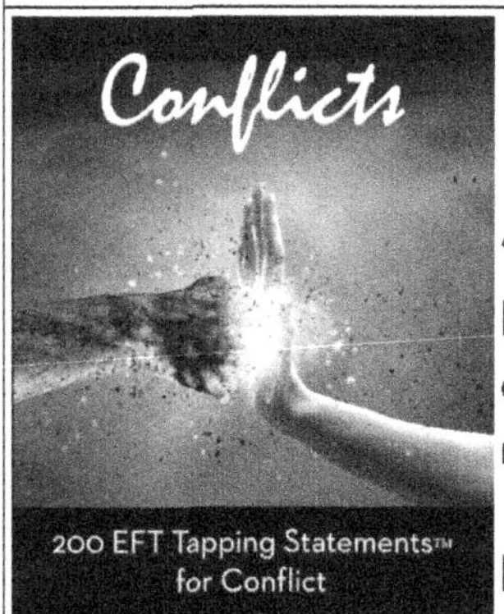


## 200 EFT Tapping Statements for Conflict

"Hi, Julia. So glad you called." Excitedly, I said, "I just finished decorating the house and I'm ready for Christmas!"

Not at all thrilled to be talking to her sister-on-law, Julia said, "That's why I'm calling. You don't mind if I host the family Christmas get-together, do you?"

A little surprised, I said, "Well, I do.

"Tough," she said. "I'm hosting Christmas this year."

This wasn't the first "conflict" with her sister-in-law. But, Audrey was a conflict coward and did not engage.

After EFT Tapping, Audrey overcame her issues with conflict. Find out how and who hosted Christmas that year!

## 80 EFT Tapping Statements for Anger

Doug was immensely proud of his son, Andy, until he watched his son (a high school senior) jeopardize his chance at an athletic scholarship to attend college. The count was 3-2, three balls and two strikes. The final pitch was thrown and Andy let it go by. The umpire shouts, "Strike!" Andy has just struck out.

"What's wrong with your eyes old man?" Andy shouts at the umpire. "That was a ball. It wasn't in the strike zone. Need instant replay so you can see it in slow motion? I'm not out!"

Andy, was following his father's example of being a rageaholic. EFT Tapping helped both Doug and Andy to take control of his life and his anger.

Anger is not right or wrong, healthy or unhealthy. It is the expression of anger that makes it right or wrong, healthy or unhealthy.

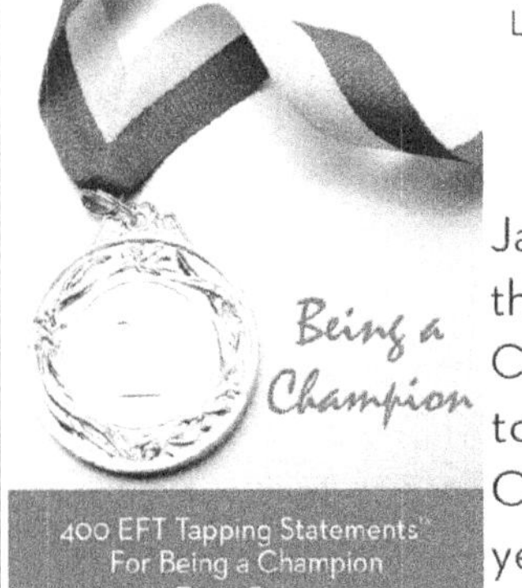


## 400 ET Tapping Statements for Being a Champion

Jack was a professional runner that injured himself at the US Championships. He was unable to compete at the World Championship. The previous year, Jack had won gold at the World Championships. After six months, he still was not able to run even though the doctors assured him he should be able to run. He had exhausted all medical and physical therapy treatments without success or hope of being able to run pain-free.

Our of frustration, Jack decided to look at the mental piece with a transformation coach. Follow Jack's recovery back to the track through EFT Tapping.

Champions are rare. If being a champion was easy then everyone would be a champion and a champion would not be anything special. It is in the difficulty of the task that, once accomplished, makes a champion great.

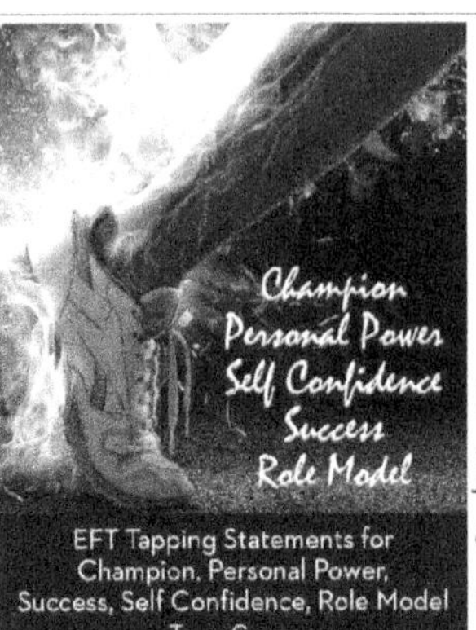


## EFT Tapping Statements for Champion, Personal Power, Success, Self Confidence, Role Model (1,000 Statements)

Being a champion is more than just being successful. It is the achievement of excellence. It is more than just being competent It is about stepping into one's power. It is more than just setting goals. It is the achievement of those goals with perseverance, dedication, and determination. It is not just about the practicing, training, and learning. It is the application and implementation of the training and learning into a competition and into everyday situations.

Champions are successful, but not all successful people are champions. Champions are powerful, but not all powerful people are champions. Champions are confident but not all confident people are champions Champions dream big but not all people that dream big are champions.

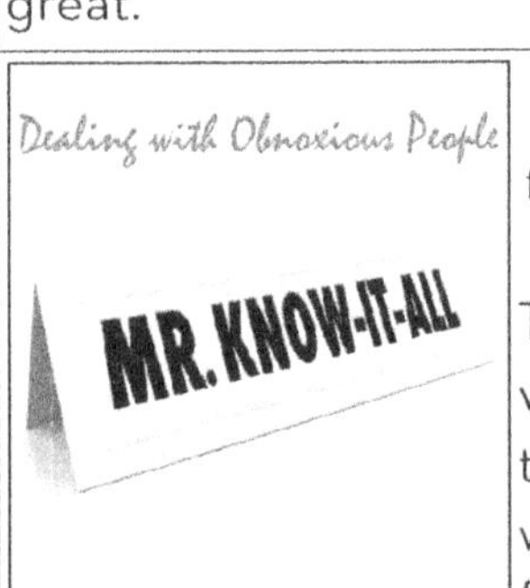


## 300 EFT Tapping Statements for Dealing with Obnoxious People

Three siblings were each dealing with an obnoxious person in their lives. Katherine was dealing with a co-worker that took credit for her accomplishments.

Megan, a professional athlete, was distracted by a narcissistic team member that disrupted practice and thus, her performances at meets.

Peter was a very successful college student that had a Teaching Assistant jealous of everything that Peter was and the TA was not.

Read how each resolved and solved their issue with an obnoxious person.

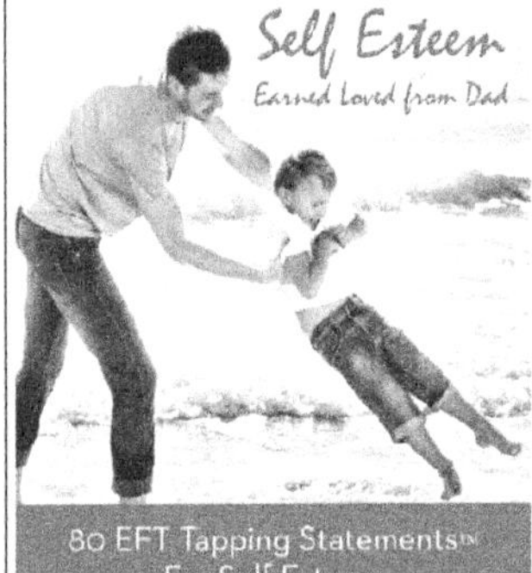


## 80 EFT Tapping Statement for Self Esteem

Ron had driven a semi-traile truck for 30 years for the sam company. To celebrate his 60t birthday and 30 years of servic his company had a celebratio for him. After the celebration Ron's boss suggested that h find a job that was more age appropriate. Ron's lack self-esteem was interfering with moving on with hi life. This book gives you the exact statements that Ro tapped to heal his lack of self esteem, self respec and self-pride.

From birth to about the age of seven, we learn sel love from mom. From about the age of seven throug twelve, from dad we learn self esteem, earned love Self esteem is about the feelings, respect, and prid we have in ourselves.

The lack of self esteem shows up in our lives as a lac self respect and/or pride in ourselves. This "lack" wi taint every area of our lives.

## 340 ET Tapping Statements for Healing From the Loss of a Loved One

Grief is more than sadness. It is more than unhappiness. Grief is a loss. Something of value is gone. Grief is an intense loss that breaks our heart. Loss can be the death of a loved one, a pet, a way of life, a job, a marriage, one's own imminent death. Grief is real.

Over time, unhealed grief becomes anger, resentment, blame, and/or remorse. We become someone that we are not. It takes courage to move through the grief and all the emotions buried deep within.

John's father died of a heart attack while gardening. A year after his death, John still was not able to move on or be happy. His wife handed him a business card of an EFT Practitioner and recommended therapy to heal the grief. After working with the Practitioner, John was able to find his joy again.

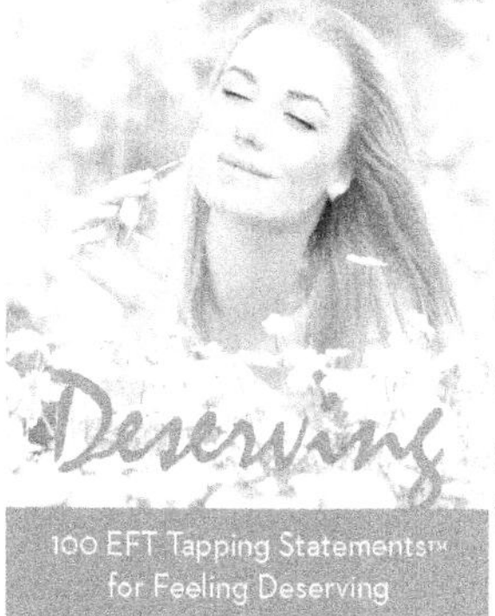


## 100 EFT Tapping Statements for Feeling Deserving

Sarah, a sophomore in college, was unsure of what to declare as her major. She met with a guidance counselor who wanted to chat first.

Sarah thought of herself as an accident since she had two older siblings who had already moved out of the house when she was five. Her parents had been looking forward to an empty nest, instead, they had a third child that was just starting school.

Sarah had felt undeserving her whole life, even though her parents loved her dearly and never treated her life an accident.

Travel the path Sarah walked with the counselor to finally feel deserving.

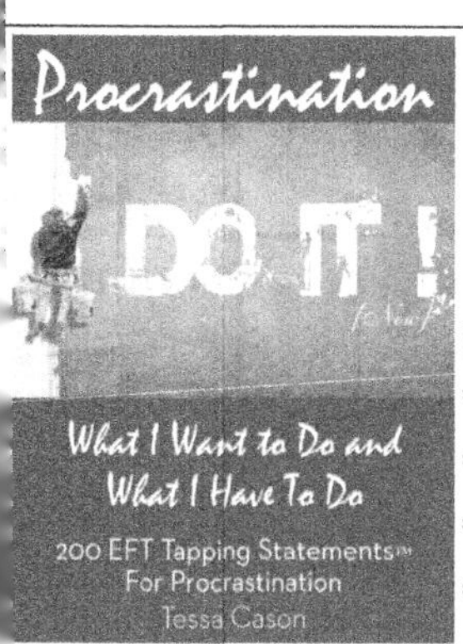


## 200 EFT Tapping Statements for Procrastination.What I Want to Do and What I Have to Do

Procrastination is about avoiding.
* What are we avoiding?
* What are we afraid to find out?
* What are we not wanting to do?
* What are we not willing to face?

Is it:
* We don't have the tools and skills to do something.
* Rebellion
* Lack of motivation.
* Not knowing what needs to be done.
* Poor time management.

The list is long why we procrastinate and what it could be about. What do we do to heal our procrastination tendencies? EFT Tapping. To heal we have to be able to recognize, acknowledge, and take ownership of that which we want to heal. Then we have to delete the dysfunctional beliefs on the subconscious level. EFT is one such tool that can do just that.

## 80 EFT Tapping Statements for Relationship with Self

Stephanie, now 55 years old, used to be excited about life and about her life. That was 35 years ago. She was engaged to the love of her life. A month before the wedding her fiancée ran off with a beauty queen.

After 35 years, Stephanie still felt defeated, beaten, defective, broken, and flawed. She was still resentful. She had become comfortable in apathy because she did not know how to move beyond her self-pity.

With the help of EFT Tapping, Stephanie was able to heal her wounded self and begin to live life again.

Do you feel disconnected from yourself? Do you feel as if you could never be whole? Do you feel defeated by life? To change our lives, we have to be able to recognize, acknowledge, and take ownership of that which we want to change. Then heal the dysfunctional beliefs on a subconscious level. EFT Tapping can help.

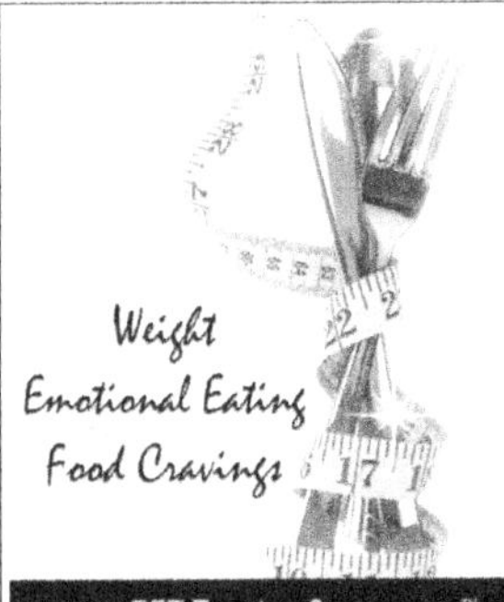


## 700 ET Tapping Statements for Weight, Emotional Eating, & Food Cravings

Emma's sister's wedding was fast approaching. She would be asked at the wedding how her diet was going.

Emma has struggled with her weight for the last 35 years, since high school. Out of desperation, Hannah began working with an EFT Practitioner. Follow her journey to healing the cause of her weight issues.

Excess weight, food cravings, emotional eating, and overeating are symptoms of deeper unresolved issues beneath the weight. Attempting to solve the problem by only dealing with the symptoms is ineffective and does not heal the issue.

Weight is the symptom. The usual programs for weight loss aren't working because they are attempting to solve the problem by dealing with the symptom instead of healing the cause.

## EFT Tapping Statements for Weight + Food Cravings, Anger, Grief, Not Good Enough, Failure (1,150 Statements)

Excess weight, food cravings, emotional eating, and overeating are symptoms of deeper issues beneath the weight. Attempting to solve the problem by only dealing with the symptoms is ineffective and does not heal the issue.

The usual programs for weight loss aren't working because they are attempting to solve the problem by dealing with the symptom instead of healing the cause.

IF WE WANT TO HEAL OUR WEIGHT ISSUES, WE NEED TO HEAL THE CAUSE...THE DYSFUNCTIONAL BELIEFS AND EMOTIONS.

HEALING IS NOT ABOUT MANAGING SYMPTOMS. IT'S ABOUT ALLEVIATING THE CAUSE OF THE SYMPTOMS.

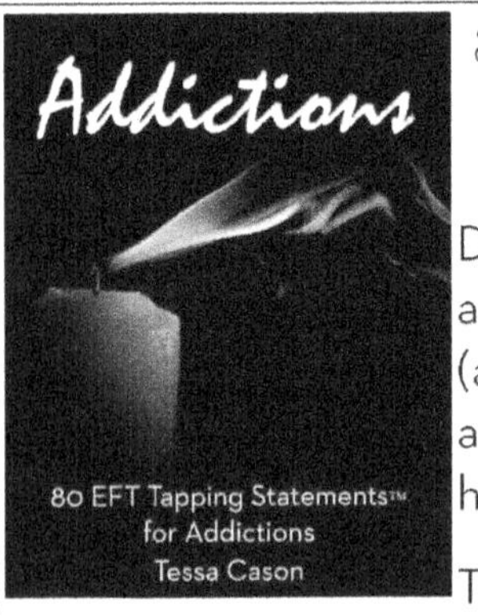


## 80 EFT Tapping Statements for Addictions

Derrick's mom died when he was a senior in high school. His dad (an alcoholic) told Derrick that as soon as he graduated from high school, he was on his own.

The day that Derrick graduated from high school, he went down and enlisted in the army. In the army, he started to drink. A month after his enlistment concluded, he met a wonderful woman. They married and had a child.

One day when Derrick returned home from the bar, he found an empty house and a note. The note told him that since has unwilling to admit he was an alcoholic or to go to counseling, she was left with only one choice. That choice was to relocate herself and their daughter to some place safe, away from him.

Derrick felt he had nothing to live for. He discovered someone at work that was a recovering alcoholic. She introduced her secret, EFT Tapping, to Derrick.

## 80 EFT Tapping Statements for Weight and Emotional Eating

Excess weight is a symptom, not the cause of overeating and emotional eating.

The day that Tracy was graduating from UCLA, she received a phone call that her father had fallen and had been hospitalized. She was on the next flight home to Dallas. It was decided that her father needed surgery and that Tracy should stay on for a short while to care for her dad. No one asked Tracy what she wanted. But, she stayed anyway.

Seven months later, even though her father had mended Tracy had become her father's caregiver. This is not what Tracy had planned to do with her life after graduating from college. Every month, over the course of the seven unhappy months, Tracy's weight spiraled up, until she was at her highest weight EVER.

This book gives you the exact statements that Tracy tapped to heal the cause of her weight gain.

## 80 ET Tapping Statements for Manifesting a Romantic Relationship

Tanya tells the story about her best friend, Nica. Nica wants a relationship. She wants to be in love, the happily-ever-after kind of love. Nica is self-absorbed, self-centered, smart, and pretty.

Nica has had several long-term relationships but, never allows anyone close enough to get to know her. When she is in between boyfriends, she always whines:

* No man will ever want me.
* The odds are slim to none that I will find anyone.
* I have a bad track record with men so I give up.
* There will never be anyone for me.
* My desires will never be fulfilled.

Tanya is a tapper and finally Nica agrees to do some tapping as a last resort! The Tapping Statements that Nica tapped to manifest a relationship are listed in this eBook.

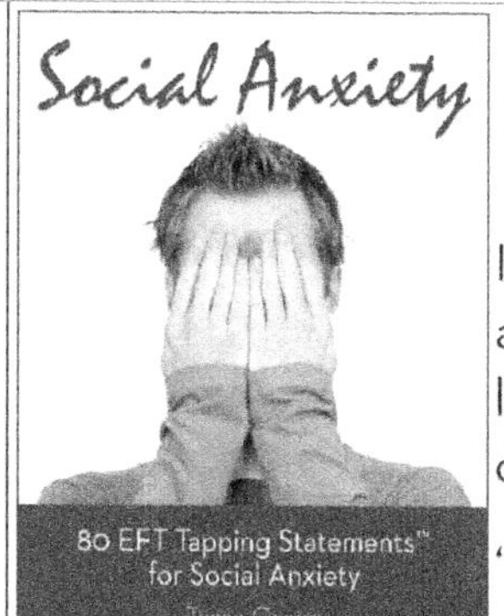


## 80 EFT Tapping Statements for Social Anxiety

In social settings, Johnny felt very awkward. He did not enjoy the limelight or any attention focused on him at all!

"Dude," Johnny's buddies would say. "When are you going to get over this fear of talking to a woman?" Johnny would laugh off their comments.

Social Anxiety - Dreading, fearing, and/or expecting to be rejected and/or humiliated by others in social settings.

* A feeling of discomfort, fear, dread, or worry that is centered on our interactions with other people.
* Fear of being judged negatively by others.
* Fear of being evaluated negatively by others.

Is there hope for those that have social anxiety? Yes. EFT Tapping. Tap the statements that Johnny tapped to overcome his social anxiety.

## 80 EFT Tapping Statements for Adult Children of Alcoholics

Did you have a parent that was an alcoholic? Do you have difficulty relating and connecting to others? Do you have a strong need to be perfect? Is your self-esteem low and judge yourself harshly? Do you have a fear of abandonment and rejection? If so, then EFT Tapping might help.

Rebecca had lost her 4th job. She was defensive, argumentative, and resentful. Rebecca knew her boss was right in firing her.

Rebecca's childhood was anything but idyllic. Her father was a raging alcoholic. She was terrified of his anger. Rebecca tried to be perfect so her dad couldn't find fault with her. Home life was hell. She had to grow up really fast and was never allow to be a kid or to play.

Rebecca did see an EFT Practitioner and was able to heal the anger, the need to be perfect, and other issues one has when they have an alcoholic parent.

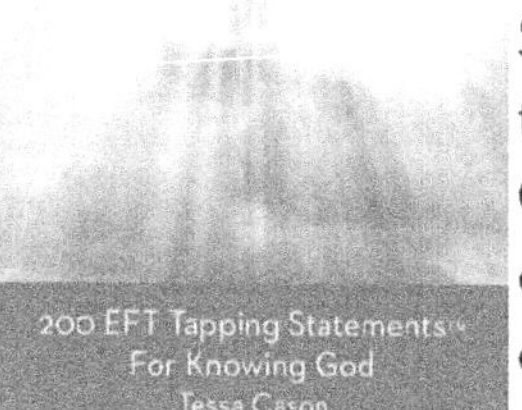


## 200 EFT Tapping Statements for Knowing God

So many questions surround this topic, God. Does God exist or is God a fabrication? Is God for real or just a concept? If God does exist, then what is God's role in our lives?

Do our prayers get answered or are we praying in vain? Does God make mistakes? God created Lucifer and then kicked out a third of his angels from heaven along with Lucifer. Was Lucifer a mistake and all the angels that choose to follow Lucifer? Do we just want to believe that a supreme being really cares about us, gave us our lives' purpose, a mission, and a destiny? God is as varied as there are people.

Many have said that God gave humans the power of choice and free will. If this is true, the consequences of our actions are ours alone. Yet, there are those who believe that God could intervene. God should take action to protect and provide for us.

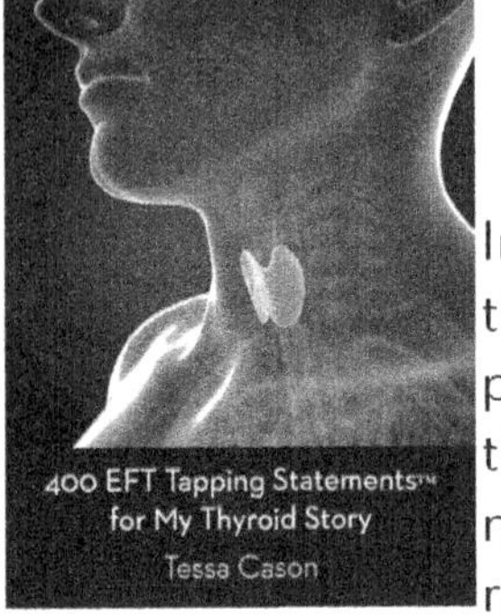


## 400 ET Tapping Statements for My Thyroid Story

In 2005, I was diagnosed with thyroid cancer. I researched the potential cause and discovered that 20 years after exposure to natural gas, thyroid issues will result. 20 years previous to the diagnosis, I lived in a townhouse for 850 days that had a gas leak.

While pursuing healing modalities after the exposure to natural gas, I began to realize that about 50% of our health issues are emotionally produced. The other 50% are the result of environmental factors such as smoking, chemicals, accidents, and/or hereditary.

I did not believe my emotional issues caused the thyroid cancer. It was the result of an environmental factor outside myself. BUT, since the thyroid was affected, if I worked on the emotional issues that had to do with the thyroid, it should impact the thyroid cancer. That was my theory.

## 100 EFT Tapping Statements for Fear of Computers

Can you image strapping on your Jet pack to get to work? Traveling on the Hyperloop that travels at speeds up to 600 mph to visit a friend that lives in another state? Stepping into your self-driving car that chauffeurs you to the restaurant? Soon all of these will be a part of our lives.

Modern technology! Most everyone knows that the computer can answer most any question. Most every job today and jobs of the future require at least some knowledge of computers.

Grandmere was intimidated by the computer. Her motivation was her granddaughter would was moving to another country. Granddaughter wants her to learn to use the computer so they can Skype when she is out of the country. Read how Grandmere was able to overcome her anxiety and fear of the computer.

## 200 EFT Tapping Statements for Sex

Is sex about the act or is sex about the intimacy shared by the act? Is sex about the orgasms or is it about the connection, touching, and cuddling?

In most culture, sex/lovemaking/intercourse is not discussed, explored, or a polite topic of conversation. For a fulfilling and satisfying sexual relationship, communication is important, yet many couples find it difficult to talk about sex.

Can you talk to your partner about sex?
Are you comfortable with your sexuality?
Do you know your partner's sexual strategy?

Our attitude, beliefs, and emotions determine our thoughts and feeling about sex. Dysfunctional beliefs can interfere with a healthy, fulfilling, satisfying sexual relationship. If we want to make changes in our lives, we have to recognize, acknowledge, and take ownership of our dysfunctional beliefs and emotions.

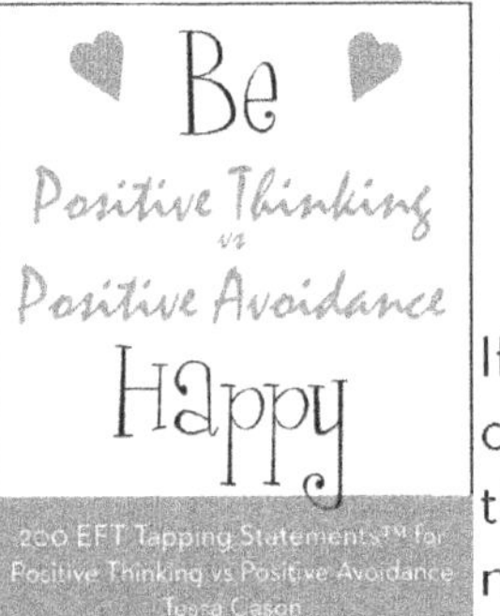


## 200 EFT Tapping Statements for Positive Thinking vs Positive Avoidance

If we keep piling more Band-Aids over a wound, the wound is still there. At some point, the wound needs to be examined, cleaned, and treated in order for heal.

Sometimes it is just "easier" to think positive when we really don't want to look at an issue. Positive Avoidance is denying the truth of a situation. It is a denial of ou experience and our feelings about the situation.

When we try to push down our negative emotions, it is like trying to push a ball underwater. The ball pops back up.

Positive Thinking is the act of thinking good or affirmative thoughts, finding the silver lining around a dark cloud, and looking on the more favorable side of an event or condition. It is not denial, avoidance, or false optimism.

# Books and Kindles eBooks by Tessa Cason

80 EFT TAPPING STATEMENTS FOR:
Abandonment
Abundance, Wealth, Money
Addictions
Adult Children of Alcoholics
Anger and Frustration
Anxiety and Worry
Change
"Less Than" and Anxiety
Manifesting a Romantic Relationship
Relationship with Self
Self Esteem
Social Anxiety
Weight and Emotional Eating

100 EFT Tapping Statements for Accepting Our Uniqueness and Being Different
100 EFT Tapping Statements for Being Extraordinary!
100 EFT Tapping Statements for Fear of Computers
100 EFT Tapping Statements for Feeling Deserving
100 EFT Tapping Statements for Feeling Fulfilled
200 EFT Tapping Statements for Conflict
200 EFT Tapping Statements for Healing a Broken Heart
200 EFT Tapping Statements for Knowing God
200 EFT Tapping Statements for Positive Thinking vs Positive Avoidance
200 EFT Tapping Statements for Procrastination
200 EFT Tapping Statements for PTSD
200 EFT Tapping Statements for Sex
200 EFT Tapping Statements for Wealth
240 EFT Tapping Statements for Fear
300 EFT Tapping Statements for Healing the Self
300 EFT Tapping Statements for Dealing with Obnoxious People
300 EFT Tapping Statements for Intuition
300 EFT Tapping Statements for Self-defeating Behaviors, Victim, Self-pity
340 EFT Tapping Statements for Healing From the Loss of a Loved One
400 EFT Tapping Statements for Being a Champion
400 EFT Tapping Statements for Being Empowered and Successful
400 EFT Tapping Statements for Dealing with Emotions
400 EFT Tapping Statements for Dreams to Reality
400 EFT Tapping Statements for My Thyroid Story

500 EFT Tapping Statements for Moving Out of Survival
700 EFT Tapping Statements for Weight, Emotional Eating, and Food Cravings
All Things EFT Tapping Manual
Emotional Significance of Human Body Parts
Muscle Testing – Obstacles and Helpful Hints

EFT Tapping Statements for:

**A Broken Heart,** Abandonment, Anger, Depression, Grief, Emotional Healing
**Anxiety**, Fear, Anger, Self Pity, Change
**Champion**, Success, Personal Power, Self Confidence, Leader/Role Model
**Prosperity,** Survival, Courage, Personal Power, Success
**PTSD**, Disempowered, Survival, Fear, Anger
**Weight & Food Cravings**, Anger, Grief, Not Good Enough, Failure

Other Books

Why we Crave What We Crave: The Archetypes of Food Cravings
How to Heal Our Food Cravings

EFT Workbook and Journal for Everyone:

Abandonment
Abundance, Money, Prosperity
Addictions
Adult Children of Alcoholics
Anger, Apathy, Guilt
Anxiety/Worry
Being A Man
Being, Doing, Belonging
Champion
Change
Conflict
Courage
Dark Forces
Decision Making
Depression
Difficult/Toxic Parents
Difficult/Toxic People
Emotional Healing

Fear
Forgiveness
God
Grief
Happiness/Joy
Intuition
Leadership
Live Your Dreams
Life Purpose/Mission
People Pleaser
Perfectionism
Personal Power
Relationship w/Others
Relationship w/Self & Commitment to Self
Self Confidence
Self Worth/Esteem
Sex
Shame
Stress
Success
Survival
Transitions
Trust/Discernment
Victim, Self-pity, Self-Defeating Behavior, Shadow Self
Weight and Emotional Eating

Made in the USA
Middletown, DE
28 July 2022

70167788R00051